BASIC

GEOMETRY

by GEORGE DAVID BIRKHOFF
Professor of Mathematics in Harvard University

and RALPH BEATLEY
Associate Professor of Education in Harvard University

AMS CHELSEA PUBLISHING
American Mathematical Society • Providence, Rhode Island

ACKNOWLEDGMENTS

The authors of this manual wish to record here their indebtedness to all those who sent in criticisms of BASIC GEOMETRY immediately following its publication. The points raised by these critics have been included in this manual. The authors are especially indebted to Professors Norman Anning and Louis C. Karpinski of the Department of Mathematics at the University of Michigan; to Professor A. A. Bennett of the Department of Mathematics at Brown University; to Professor Harold Fawcett of the College of Education at Ohio State University; to Mr. G. E. Hawkins of the Lyons Township High School and Junior College, La Grange, Illinois; to Mr. Francis W. Runge of the New School of Evanston Township High School, Evanston, Illinois; and to Miss Margaret Lord of the high school at Lawrence, Massachusetts.

Library of Congress Catalog Card Number 49-2197
International Standard Book Number 978-0-8218-2692-8

INTRODUCTION

BASIC GEOMETRY aims to give the pupil an appreciation of logical method and a skill in logical argument that he can and will apply in non-mathematical situations. It aims also to present a system of demonstrative geometry that, while serving as a pattern of all abstract logical systems, is much simpler and more compact than Euclid's geometry or than any geometry since Euclid.

The underlying spirit of BASIC GEOMETRY, as geometry, can be set forth best by contrasting it with Euclid's geometry. In Euclid, congruence and parallelism are fundamental and similarity is secondary, being derived from parallelism. But since similarity is used more than parallelism in proofs, and since congruence and similarity have much in common, it seems more natural to take these two ideas as fundamental and to derive parallelism from them. If we make an exchange of this sort, the Parallel Postulate becomes a theorem on parallels, and one of the former theorems on similar triangles becomes a postulate. A geometric system of this sort was suggested in 1923 in the British Report on the Teaching of Geometry in Schools, mentioned below. BASIC GEOMETRY carries the idea even farther by using only a postulate of similarity and treating congruence - we say equality instead - as a special case under similarity for which the factor of proportionality is 1.

The history of the development of this geometry is of interest, to show how mathematical ideas sometimes come to light, are sidetracked or forgotten, and come to light again centuries later. As early as 1733 Saccheri proved in his Euclides ab omni naevo Vindicatus, Prop. 21, Schol. 3, that a single postulate of similarity is sufficient to establish all the usual ideas concerning parallels. He gives credit* to John Wallis, Savilian Professor of Geometry at Oxford from 1649 to 1703,

---

*See Halsted's translation of Saccheri's Euclides ab omni naevo Vindicatus, Open Court, Chicago, 1920, page 105.

- 1 -

for announcing this idea and for showing that Euclid could have rearranged his Elements so as to follow this order. The idea appeared again in Couturat's La Logique de Leibniz, 1900, and in the British Report on the Teaching of Geometry in Schools, which was presented and accepted on November 3, 1923 and published before the end of 1923 by G. Bell and Sons, London.

In the spring of this same year, 1923, Professor Birkhoff was invited to deliver in Boston a series of Lowell Lectures on Relativity. In order to present this subject with as few technicalities as possible he decided to devise the simplest possible system of Euclidean geometry he could think of, and - without any acquaintance at that time with any earlier enunciation of the idea of a postulate of similarity - he hit upon the framework of the system that, with all the details filled in, is now BASIC GEOMETRY. The postulates of this geometry were first printed in Chapter 2 of Birkhoff's book The Origin, Nature, and Influence of Relativity, Macmillan, 1925, which reports these lectures of two years earlier. It is interesting that John Wallis' idea of a Similarity Postulate should have come to light again in England and in the United States in 1923, quite independently and almost simultaneously. As a result of inquiry in England the authors believe that BASIC GEOMETRY is the first and only detailed elaboration of this idea for use in secondary schools.

The authors recognize the need of passing the pupil through two preliminary stages before plunging him into the serious study of a logical system of geometry. First, the pupil must acquire a considerable familiarity with the facts of geometry in the junior high school years in order the better to appreciate the chief aim of demonstrative geometry, which is not fact but demonstration. In order to emphasize this contrast it is well that there should be a distinct gap between the factual

- 2 -

geometry of the junior high school and the demonstrative geometry of the senior high school. Certain authors of books on demonstrative geometry, recognizing that some pupils enter upon this subject with very little knowledge of the facts of geometry, try to make good this deficiency through an introductory chapter on factual geometry. The authors of BASIC GEOMETRY have preferred not to do this because they are fearful that the distinction between fact and demonstration will be blurred if the proofs of important but "obvious" propositions follow immediately after an intuitional treatment of these same ideas. The proper solution of this problem is to provide adequate instruction in informal geometry in the seventh and eighth grades. The educational grounds in support of such a program lie far deeper than mere preparation for demonstrative geometry in a later grade. Fortunately the increasing tendency to give more instruction in informal geometry in the seventh and eighth grades is gradually eliminating the need for an introductory treatment of factual geometry at the beginning of demonstrative geometry.

The second preliminary stage through which the pupil must pass is a brief introduction to the logical aspects of demonstrative geometry. This includes discussion of the need of undefined terms, defined terms, and assumptions in any logical system, and also includes a brief exemplification of a logical treatment of geometry - a miniature demonstrative geometry, in effect - in order to exhibit the nature of geometric proof, and to afford an easy transition to the systematic logical development that is to follow. It is introductory material of this sort that constitutes the first chapter of BASIC GEOMETRY.

The logical aims of BASIC GEOMETRY are of two sorts: to give boys and girls an understanding of correct logical method in arguments whose scope is narrowly restricted, and to give an appreciation of the nature and requirements of logical systems in the large. In order to attain the first of these aims this book lays great stress on the nature of proof. It uses geometric ideas as a source of clear and unambiguous examples, and as a rich source of materials for practice. It also encourages the transfer to non-geometric situations of the skills and appreciations learned first in a geometric setting.

In order to attain the second logical aim this book calls frequent attention to its own logical structure; it contrasts its own structure with that of other geometries; and it emphasizes the important features common to all logical systems. It dares even to call attention to certain loopholes in its own logic, using footnotes or veiled allusions in the running text to mark the spots where the geometric fox has run to cover from the hot pursuit of the geometric hounds. These are mentioned in this manual also, often with additional comment.

BASIC GEOMETRY not only exhibits a logical system that is simpler and more rigorous than that contained in any other geometry used in our schools; its system is also the very simplest and the most rigorously logical that pupils in our secondary schools can be expected to understand and appreciate. In one or two instances the authors have wittingly allowed a slight logical blemish to remain in the text when the point at issue was of a nature to be apparent only to adults and was so remote from the interests of secondary school pupils that the substitution of an absolutely correct statement would have made the book too involved and too difficult at that point. Each logical blemish recognized as such by the authors will be discussed at the proper time in this manual to clarify the logical structure of the text as fully as possible. Teachers who are interested to see what a rigorous treatment of this geometry demands can find the logical framework in an article by George D. Birkhoff in the Annals of Mathematics, Vol. XXXIII, April, 1932, entitled "A Set of Postulates for Plane Geometry, Based on Scale and Protractor."

An article by Birkhoff and Beatley in The Fifth Yearbook of the National Council of Teachers of Mathematics, 1930, gives a brief description of BASIC GEOMETRY on an elementary level, and compares it with other geometries.

The chief advantage of BASIC GEOMETRY is that it gets to the heart of demonstrative geometry more quickly than other texts. It is able to do this by postulating the proposition that if two triangles have an angle of one equal to an angle of the other and the including sides proportional, the triangles are similar. This leads simultaneously to the basic theorems under equality and similarity and immediately thereafter to the theorems concerning the sum of the angles of a triangle, the essence of the perpendicular-bisector locus without using the word "locus," and the Pythagorean Theorem - all within the first seven theorems. BASIC GEOMETRY contains only thirty-three "book theorems." A few of these, at crucial points, embrace the content of two or more theorems of the ordinary school texts, as is hinted by the postulate on triangles mentioned above. This accounts for the great condensation of content into brief compass.

If it be objected that other books could reduce their lists of theorems also by telescoping some and calling others exercises, the proper answer is that every book recognizes that the chief instructional value of demonstrative geometry is to be found in the "original" exercises and tries therefore to reduce the number of its book theorems. But these other books just have to exhibit the proofs of lots of theorems because otherwise the pupils would not figure out how to prove them. They could of course be called exercises, but the pupils could not handle the exercises, so-called.

In BASIC GEOMETRY, however, the fundamental principles and basic theorems are of such wide applicability that the pupil can actually use

- 5 -

these tools _to prove as exercises_ most of the propositions that other books **must** carry as book theorems. With all the usual ideas concerning equal and similar triangles, angle-sum, perpendicular bisector, and Pythagorean Theorem available at the outset, it would be ridiculous for BASIC GEOMETRY to retain as book theorems what other books must so retain. We do indeed require six book theorems on parallel and perpendicular lines, six more on the circle, three or five (depending on the system one follows) on area, four on continuous variation, and the usual locus theorems. Almost all these book theorems follow very easily from the twelve basic postulates and theorems. Not more than five of these book theorems are at all hard, and three of these hard ones are proved in the same way as in other books. In short, there is a real reason for calling this book "Basic Geometry."

Ideally, every exercise in this book can be deduced from the five fundamental principles and the thirty-three book theorems; but there is no objection to using an exercise, once proved, as a link in the logical chain on which a later exercise depends. This holds for other geometries as well.

A further advantage of BASIC GEOMETRY is its willingness to take for granted the real number system, assuming that the pupil has already had some experience with irrational numbers in arithmetic - though not by name - and has a sound intuitive notion of irrationals. In this respect pupils of the eighth grade in this country today are way ahead of Euclid's contemporaries and we ought to capitalize this advantage. The theorems of this geometry, therefore, are equally valid for incommensurable and commensurable cases without need of limits.

Although BASIC GEOMETRY seems to require five fundamental postulates in Chapter 2 and two more postulates on area in Chapter 7, it is clear from pages 50, 198, 199, and 222 that this system of geometry really

- 6 -

requires only four postulates. These postulates are set forth as Principles 1, 2, 3, and 5. It should be noted, as the authors indicate on page 278, Exercise 4, that Principle 6 of BASIC GEOMETRY, instead of Principle 5, could have been taken as the fundamental Postulate of Similarity. But Principle 5 is to be preferred for this role, for reasons of fundamental simplicity.

This discussion of the order of the assumptions and theorems of this geometry raises the question of how to reconcile the psychologically desirable ideal of allowing the pupils to suggest the propositions they wish to assume at the outset with the mathematical ideal of insuring that any system the pupils construct for themselves shall be reasonably free from gross errors. It is probably well to let the pupils spend a little time in constructing their own systems provided the teacher is competent to indicate the major errors and omissions in each system that the pupils put together; for careful elucidation of the reasons why certain arrangements of geometric ideas will eventually prove faulty can be very instructive.

This is only one of many situations in the teaching of mathematics where psychology and mathematics are in conflict. We have a second instance in our attempt to devise a psychologically proper _inductive_ approach to a logically _deductive_ science. Many teachers who recognize the value of trial-and-error in the learning process hesitate to apply to the learning of so precise a subject as mathematics the method of fumbling and stumbling that seems to be the universal method by which human beings learn anything new. The really good teacher of mathematics rejoices in this eternal challenge to him to reconcile irreconcilables. He dares to begin precise subjects like algebra and demonstrative geometry with a certain degree of nonchalance. He does not try to tell the pupil every detail when considering the first equation, but prefers to

- 7 -

consider the solution of several equations in fairly rapid succession and trusts in that manner gradually to build up the correct doctrine. He does not insist on technical verbiage at the outset. He leapfrogs dreary book theorems in geometry and plunges into a consideration of easy originals, trusting that by so doing the pupils will acquire inductively a feel for logical deduction. He will not hamper this early learning by insisting on stereotyped procedures, whether with equations in algebra or with proofs in geometry. And yet, with all this desirable nonchalance at the outset, he must know when and how to question his early procedures of this sort and must lead his pupils eventually to amplify and amend them.

BASIC GEOMETRY was used for seven years in regular classes in the high school at Newton, Massachusetts, before it was published in its present form. To a teacher whose earlier experience with geometry differs from this presentation it is admittedly somewhat confusing at the outset. Because of this earlier experience of a different sort the teacher will often make hard work of an exercise that seems straightforward and simple to the student. An excellent example of this is to be found on page 115, Exercise 22. Originally Fig. 11 carried a dotted line EF parallel to AB. This was inserted by one of the authors to lead the pupils toward the proof. But the pupils needed no such help, using Principle 5 at once. This line EF was a result of the author's earlier training in geometry. After this had been pointed out by Mr. Enoch in one of the first years of the Newton experiment, the dotted line was expunged, but so reluctantly that the letter F hung on through the first printing of the book. The students do not have this sort of difficulty. Consequently, a teacher in his first experience with BASIC GEOMETRY will do well to observe the methods used by his pupils.

- 8 -

Students of average ability and better, the sort who succeed in ordinary courses in geometry, will be at least equally successful with BASIC GEOMETRY. It is the common experience of teachers using this book that classes get into the heart of geometry much more quickly than when a book of the conventional kind is used. Pupils whose ability is below average, the sort who tend to memorize under conventional instruction and pick up a mumbo-jumbo of geometric jargon without really knowing what it is all about, will find that BASIC GEOMETRY offers little field for memorizing and sets no store by technical jargon. Such pupils either catch the spirit of BASIC GEOMETRY and win a moderate success, or they drop out early in the race. The real loss under BASIC GEOMETRY is no greater than in conventional classes; the apparent loss is admittedly greater, because BASIC GEOMETRY - with its brief list of "book theorems" and its insistence on "original exercises" - offers little refuge and scant reward to a pretense of understanding. But anyone who profits genuinely from a conventional course will derive at least an equal, and probably a greater, profit from BASIC GEOMETRY.

Students who use this book and then go on to solid geometry are not handicapped by their unusual training in plane geometry. If anything, they do better than students who have studied plane geometry in the conventional way. This is borne out by the experience of Mr. Mergendahl, head of the department at Newton High School, who has regularly taught solid geometry to classes composed of pupils some of whom have had a conventional course in plane geometry while others were brought up on BASIC GEOMETRY. This is as nearly impartial evidence as we can get; for Mr. Mergendahl has not used BASIC GEOMETRY in his own classes, though he was responsible for initiating this experiment at Newton and has encouraged it and followed it with a highly intelligent interest.

- 9 -

The following time schedule will serve to guide the teacher in his first experience with this book.

```
Chapter 1---------------------9 periods
Chapter 2--------------------15 periods
Chapter 3--------------------19 periods
Chapter 4--------------------12 periods
Chapter 5--------------------27 periods
Chapter 6--------------------19 periods
Chapter 7--------------------17 periods
Chapter 8---------------------6 periods
Chapter 9--------------------14 periods
Chapter 10-------------------7 periods
                           145 periods
```

This schedule is based on a school year of at least 34 solid working weeks, with four 50-minute (or longer) periods a week devoted to geometry. If the course can be spread over two years, with at least 68 periods each year devoted to geometry, the pupils will learn and retain more than if the 145 periods of geometry are concentrated in one year. This extension of the calendar time during which the pupil is exposed to this subject will also help the other subject with which the geometry presumably alternates. Ordinarily this other subject will be second-year algebra. Under this alternative a good procedure is to devote all four periods for the first two or three weeks of the first year to the geometry until the course is well started and then to alternate with algebra, doing geometry on Monday and Tuesday, for example, and algebra on Thursday and Friday of each week.

One last word before we proceed to consider this book chapter by chapter. The introduction, the footnotes, the summaries at the ends of the chapters, the Laws of Number, and the index are intended to help the teacher in presenting this novel course in geometry and reasoning to secondary school pupils. The authors suggest that teachers make full use of these aids.

George David Birkhoff

Ralph Beatley

C H A P T E R 1

Lesson Plan Outline: 9 lessons

1-2. Through page 19, Ex. 2

3. Exs. 3-7, pages 19-20

4. Discuss theorems A, B, and C in class and
assign page 24, Exs. 1, 2, and 5

5. Exs. 3, 4, and 6, pages 24-25

6. Converse propositions, and Exs. 1-11, page 28

7-9. Pages 29-36

The authors intend that the pupils will read and discuss this chapter
in class, section by section, doing some of the exercises in class and
others outside of class. The pupils ought also to reread the text quiet-
ly by themselves outside of class and make a conscious effort to remember
the main ideas of the chapter. Chapter 1 is introductory in character
and fundamentally important for all that follows. Nevertheless, complete
appreciation of this chapter will come only after the pupil has gone
deeply into the succeeding chapters. Consequently it will be better not
to plod too painstakingly through Chapter 1 at the start, but to try instead to take in its main features fairly rapidly and then return to it
from time to time for careful study as questions arise concerning the
place of undefined terms, defined terms, assumptions, theorems, converses,
and so on, in a logical system.

Page 14, line 3: "Equal" versus "Congruent." The system of geometry set
forth in Chapters 2-9 makes no use of superposition and does not require
the term "congruent," which some other authors think they need. These
other authors take "rigid," "motion," and "coincide throughout" as undefined terms, though they do not declare them to be such. They then say
that if, by a rigid motion, two figures can be made to coincide throughout, they are "congruent"; and if congruent, that all corresponding

- 11 -

parts of the two figures are "equal." By "parts" they usually mean line-segments and angles. So now we know what "equal" means, at least when applied to geometric figures that are parts of other geometric figures. These authors could have applied the term "equal" to the congruent wholes as well as to their corresponding parts. But, as we shall see, many of them do not permit this use of "equal" with respect to two geometric figures that are momentarily regarded as wholes, even though these same geometric figures can be regarded also as parts of other figures. In sum, these authors define "congruent" and "equal" in terms of "rigid motion" and "coincide." Whole figures can be congruent; partial figures can be both congruent and equal.

Possibly this strange distinction had its origin in the desire to prove the equality of the measures of line-segments, or angles, by showing the line-segments, or angles, to be corresponding parts of congruent figures. Interest was centered not so much in the geometric configurations as in the numbers that measured them. But Euclidean habit confused line-segment and its measure, and angle and its measure; and this habit has persisted to the present time. Though line-segments are called equal, it is their lengths that are meant. It would appear then that two triangles cannot be called equal unless these geometric figures also have some characteristic numerical measure in common. Since a triangle encloses a part of its plane, its area seems to be a more significant measure than its perimeter, which is but a composite of the lengths of the line-segment sides. If this is the reason for calling two triangles equal only when they are equal in area, it seems hardly adequate.

The undefined idea - really two ideas - of rigid motion implies motion without distortion; that is to say, without resulting inequality. Inherent in the undefined term "rigid" is the idea "equal" that later will be defined in terms of it. If it were proper to challenge the undefined

- 12 -

term "coincide" and inquire what is the criterion for testing perfect fit, in order to distinguish between an apparent fit within some recognized limit of error and a genuine errorless fit, can one imagine an answer that does not involve equality? Of these four ideas, rigid motion, coincide, congruent, and equal, does one stand out as clearly more fundamental than the others? The authors of BASIC GEOMETRY say, "Yes, equal." Other authors say, "Rigid motion." Let us see how these other authors proceed.

If two triangles have an angle of one equal to an angle of the other and the including sides also equal, we can bid one triangle remain rigid and can move it so that certain parts of it fall on - more or less - the corresponding parts of the other triangle. Can these corresponding parts then be made to coincide? It is so asserted. Why? Because they were given equal. It appears that if two line-segments or angles are equal and stay equal while in motion, then they can be made to coincide. The rest of the ceremony concerning these triangles consists of showing that the third pair of sides coincide, and hence are equal; and that the other two pairs of angles are equal also, because coincident.

We have seen first that three pairs of parts coincide because they are equal, and then that three other pairs are equal because they coincide. What then is the distinction between congruent and equal? Let us look further.

Some followers of the "congruent" school insist that two parallelograms that are not congruent can be equal. When they apply the term equal to two "whole" figures of this sort, they mean equal in area. Occasionally the whole figures may be congruent, but ordinarily not. An adult layman would never call two such figures equal, whose corresponding parts are ordinarily unequal and whose only common property is their area. If this is the important distinction between congruent and equal wholes,

- 13 -

no wonder that pupils who are just beginning demonstrative geometry are baffled by its mysteries.

The authors of BASIC GEOMETRY regard the term "equal" (see pages 39 and 285) as familiar to everyone and not requiring to be defined. Taken as undefined, it can be applied immediately to numbers, and also to geometric figures that are wholes, as well as to figures that are parts of wholes, just as everybody would normally expect.

Incidentally it must be clear why the authors of BASIC GEOMETRY are glad to avoid proving a "side-angle-side" theorem at the very beginning of demonstrative geometry, and prefer to include the content of this proposition in a fundamental assumption, Case I of Similarity. See BASIC GEOMETRY, pages 59-60.

Pages 14-15: Circle, diameter. Unfortunately, mathematicians do not always adhere to their own canons of accuracy with respect to terminology. Occasionally they wink at certain inaccuracies and inconsistencies and agree, in effect, to confuse colloquial and technical usage. It is necessary that pupils should know which mathematical terms are sometimes used loosely; for example, circle, circumference, diameter, radius, altitude, and median.

At first blush it seems as though the strict meaning of "diameter" must be "through-measure," a number and not a line. But inasmuch as Euclid represented numbers by line-segments, the "through-measure" of a circle was to the Greeks a line-segment containing the center of the circle and terminated by the circle, or another line-segment equal to this. This ambiguity has probably led the makers of dictionaries to put the line idea ahead of the number idea. The ambiguous terms radius, diameter, altitude, and median are treated consistently in this book.

Page 15: "Things equal to the same thing. . .." We are not eager that pupils should adopt this wording, but all teachers know it and many of

- 14 -

them will wish their pupils to use it. It is a property of the undefined idea "equal" and is postulated for that purpose. (See pages 39 and 285.) In this book we do not give any reason in support of statements like "PQ = PQ." Where other books say "By identity" or "Identical," we say nothing. One of the postulates governing the use of the symbol = for the undefined term "equal" is "a = a." (See page 285.)

Pages 16-17: Exercises. As noted at the bottom of page 15, the students will need to consult a dictionary here. The teacher should remind his pupils that in mathematics a dictionary can often be of assistance if only they will think to use one.

Answers are omitted for exercises where the correct answer is fairly obvious to the teacher.

2. "Light cream" is heavier. "Thin cream" and "thick cream."

3. Sugar dissolves in coffee, and butter melts in hot oyster stew.

   Solid or frozen substances whose melting point is below body temperature, namely 98.6°F.

   The oil dissolves in the gasoline.

9. South also.

Page 17: Assumptions. A proposition is merely an assertion; it is devoid of truth value. Propositions are of two sorts: those that we assume, variously called assumptions, postulates, axioms; and those that we can deduce from the assumptions. These latter are called theorems. One person's theorem may be another person's assumption. It is the logical relation, not the verbal content, of any given proposition that classifies it as assumption or theorem.

Page 18: "4 x 8 = 28." If this example leads to momentary consideration of number systems with base different from 10, let the teacher be warned that expressions like 4 x 8 = 52 and 4 x 8 = 57 must be avoided; they will not have the meanings that pupils will wish to ascribe to them.

For, while 4 x 8 = (5 x 6) + 2 in our ordinary arithmetic, we cannot write 4 x 8 = 52 in the number system to the base 6 because that system has no 8. Similarly, while 4 x 8 = (5 x 5) + 7 in our arithmetic, neither 8 nor 7 appears in the number system to the base 5.

Pages 19-20: Exercises.

1. a, d   2. c, b   3. d, a   4. b, c

5. Solid ludge sinks in molten runk. Or, solid runk floats on molten ludge.

6. True if base is 5.

7. That the government chose to test the twelve best of all brands of weather-strip manufactured, and that among these twelve the rating of 93% efficient was very high.

Page 20: The Nature of Geometric Proof. It must be emphasized that the three assumptions on this page, Theorems A, B, and C that follow, and the theorems in the Exercises on pages 24-25 are not part of the official geometry of this book. They constitute a miniature geometry to show the logical relation between assumption and theorem, and to afford an example - intentionally a bit casual - of the proof of a theorem. This is _not_ the place for the teacher to begin to insist on certain procedures in proving theorems, such as separating statements and reasons into two clearly divided columns, or to insist on the use of certain technical terms and phrases. Our goal in teaching geometry - and it is a difficult one to attain - is to elicit clear thinking. While there is undoubtedly a definite connection between clear thinking and clear expression, the parrot-like repetition by pupils of accurate statements insisted on by textbook or teacher is all too often an obstruction to thinking. It is admittedly not easy to combine accuracy of thought with informality of expression, but this combination is psychologically desirable at the beginning. Indeed, if the pupil is to be encouraged to transfer his skill in reasoning from geometry to non-mathematical situations, it would be well to relieve him for all time of the requirement of learning a rigmarole of proof that is peculiar to geometry (under some teachers) and has no counterpart in other walks of life. Specifically, the artificial separation of statements and reasons by a vertical line drawn down the page can be a definite handicap to the transfer of learning in geometric situations to other situations in which the reasons in support of an argument are commonly incorporated in an ordinary paragraph. Admittedly the vertical line makes it easier for the teacher to check the pupil's work and this consideration deserves some weight. Possibly a compromise can be effected here, whereby the pupil is asked to submit proofs in paragraph form once or twice a week, understanding that this is the ideal form for submitting arguments in general, and is asked to use the vertical line at other times in order to save the teacher's time.

There is no need to add to the three assumptions on page 20 a fourth assumption to the effect that the corresponding parts of equal triangles are equal, for all this is implied by the term "equal," which we take as undefined. Surely the word "equal" carries universally the implication that corresponding parts of equals are equal. (See pages 57, 59, and 60.)

Page 22: Hypothesis, Conclusion. It is important to note that line 7 does not say that the hypothesis is co-extensive with the "if-part" of the statement of a proposition. Usually the "if-part" contains the "universe of discourse" as well as the particular condition of the proposition. By implication the universe of discourse is a part also of the conclusion, though it is usually not included in the "then-part." For example, in the proposition "If a quadrilateral is a parallelogram, the diagonals bisect each other" the universe of discourse is the quadrilateral, the thing we are talking about. The universe of discourse is still

- 17 -

the quadrilateral when the proposition is stated in the form "The diagonals of a parallelogram bisect each other."

Unfortunately the English language often permits more than one way of writing a proposition in "If- - - , then- - -"form. There is no hard and fast rule by which the teacher can circumvent these ambiguities. This subject is considered at greater length on pages 28-33 of this manual as part of the discussion on the framing of converse propositions.

While it is convenient and important to refer to the "If - - -, then - - -" form, the teacher should note that the "then" is usually omitted. We have indicated this on page 22 by enclosing the "then" in parentheses.

Although the "If- - - , then- - - " form is characteristic of deductive reasoning, the teacher should recognize that it is employed also in inductive thinking. He should be ready, therefore, to dispel this possible cause of confusion when induction is considered on pages 273-276.

It is not enough that the pupil shall know how to write a geometric proposition in "If- - - , then- - - " form. He must be able also to translate the words of the proposition into a proper geometric figure. To see that he acquires this ability is only one of the many important functions of the teacher.

Page 21: Theorem A. Some teachers will think that the analysis of this theorem, presumably the first that the pupil has ever met, is disposed of too quickly; and similarly in Theorems B and C. It is our studied policy, however, to exhibit several proofs in fairly rapid succession, so that the pupil may get a rough idea of what is expected, and then to provide exercises immediately thereafter on which he can try his hand. We are much more interested that he "get the hang of the thing" right from the start than that he dwell on details. We would employ an inductive method in teaching deduction by showing a few deductions and

- 18 -

allowing the pupil to induce what he can of deduction from them. Then
let him learn more "by doing."

A false lead - but a perfectly natural one - was purposely introduced
into the analysis of Theorem A. We want to encourage the pupil in trial-
and-error thinking and wish to avoid giving the impression that we are
setting up a model proof in final form and expecting him to follow the
pattern closely. It seems to us that the schools have done enough dam-
age by beginning demonstrative geometry in that way for the last hundred
years. We are not content to show the pupil one correct method of proof;
we wish also to show him "why it cannot be done his way," and to indicate
that a few changes in the preliminary set-up would make his way just as
good as ours. A pupil who is trained to consider the relation of every
proof to the body of assumptions from which he is working will gain both
understanding and appreciation of the nature of proof. Teachers of geometry, committees, and commissions say that we ought to do this. Very
well, here it is!

Page 23: "Logical refinements." Of course, in this miniature geometry which we present here in Chapter 1 in order to give the student some
notion of the nature of logical proof, we have already made clear on
page 20 that we need to borrow certain definitions from the main body of
this geometry. Similarly, we need to borrow certain implications of the
Principles of Line Measure and of Angle Measure that appear later in the
main geometry. We have chosen not to be too rigorous here in order not
to distract the pupil from our main purpose. We have, however, chosen
to insert a remark on page 23 that implies that even when we get serious
in developing the main geometry of this book, we shall even then put a
limit to rigor and shall ignore certain fine points. We believe, nevertheless, that BASIC GEOMETRY is more rigorous than other geometries pre-
pared for secondary schools, and that it sets a good example in calling

- 19 -

attention openly to those instances where the logical rigor is relaxed, and in indicating in the text, or in a footnote, or in the Manual for Teachers, just what is involved.

The logical refinements that "we usually ignore" concern the existence of the midpoint of a line-segment, the existence of the bisector of an angle, the existence of a unique perpendicular to a line at a point of the line, and the five theorems listed below. In BASIC GEOMETRY the three existence theorems just mentioned are special instances of the Principles of Line Measure and of Angle Measure. As will be shown in the comments on Chapter 2, they follow immediately from the fact that the Principles of Line Measure and of Angle Measure involve the System of Real Numbers in a fundamental manner. Consequently BASIC GEOMETRY has no difficulty with hypothetical constructions, with which other systems of geometry are plagued. That is, other geometries would like to prove in advance the existence of certain points and lines that they need in the proofs of certain theorems, and not merely take these existence ideas for granted. If they adhere to this program faithfully they find it hard to avoid "reasoning in a circle"; or, if they escape this logical error, it is only by constructing a sequence of theorems that seems to the beginning student to be quite devoid of order and of sense.

The intimate association of the system of real numbers with the Principles of Line Measure and of Angle Measure not only establishes the crucial points and lines we need at the beginning, and so removes all question of hypothetical constructions from BASIC GEOMETRY; it also enables us to prove certain fundamental theorems like the five listed below that are assumptions, but unmentioned assumptions, of Euclid's Elements and of ordinary systems of geometry since Euclid. In BASIC GEOMETRY we choose to ignore fundamental theorems of this sort because both the content and proof are remote from the interests of secondary school pupils.

It should be emphasized, however, that these fundamental ideas that we choose to ignore for pedagogic reasons are theorems that can be proved in BASIC GEOMETRY. Our failure to mention them explicitly in the book forces them conceivably into the same category as Principle 4, the converse of Principle 9 (page 84), and the two area assumptions on page 199; but all of these can be deduced from Principles 1, 2, 3, and 5 of BASIC GEOMETRY. They are temporary assumptions by choice, and not - as in other geometries - permanent assumptions by necessity.

The five fundamental theorems referred to, each of which is proved by means of the continuity inherent in the system of real numbers, are as follows:

(1) That a plane is divided into two parts by any line in the plane.

(2) That a straight line joining points A_1 and A_2, on opposite sides of line 1, must have a point in common with 1.

(3) That every line that contains a point P on one of the sides of triangle ABC and does not contain a vertex must have a point in common with one of the other two sides of the triangle.

(4) That a line joining a point inside a circle and a point outside the circle must have a point in common with the circle.

(5) That a circular arc b joining a point inside a circle a to a point outside circle a must have a point in common with circle a.

These five theorems are proved in the following manner, making free use of the continuity of the system of real numbers. The methods used will indicate how other similar fundamental ideas can be established that are not mentioned here but that may occur to teachers as they study the foundations of geometry.

Fundamental Theorem 1. A plane is divided into two parts by any line in the plane. That is, the points of the plane are divided by the line into three classes, those "on one side" of the line, those on the line, and those "on the other side" of the line; whence those points on one side of the line and those points not on this same side of the line constitute the two parts of the plane referred to.

Proof: Consider a random point O on line $\underline{l}$. Connect O with other points A in the plane that are not on $\underline{l}$. These connecting line segments make angles θ with $\underline{l}$ that differ from 0, π, or 2π because these points A are never on $\underline{l}$. We can divide these points A into two classes:

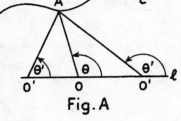

Fig. A

(1) those for which $0 < \theta < \pi$, and

(2) those for which $\pi < \theta < 2\pi$,

where $\theta = \theta$ (modulo 2π). We shall call the points of the first class A_1's, and those of the second class A_2's. From our Principle of Angle Measure (page 47) amplified as on page 231* we see that as A varies continuously through many suitably chosen points A_1, such as the points of the curve c in Fig. A, θ varies continuously through a range of values that are always between 0 and π.

Now consider another random point O' on line $\underline{l}$ and join O' to all the points A_1 just traversed by A. The angle θ' varies continuously also, but can never equal π; for if it did, A_1 would lie on $\underline{l}$, which is impossible. This means that for all A_1, if θ' ever has a value less than π, it can never take a value greater than π, and conversely; for if it could, then θ', in varying continuously, would have to equal π momentarily. Consequently, as point A traverses a series

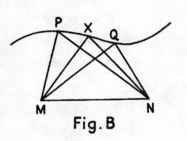

Fig. B

----
*Namely, if in Fig. B, M and N are fixed while X varies continuously from P to Q, then angles MXN, XNM, and NMX vary continuously also.

of points A_1, indeed <u>all</u> the points A_1, θ is between 0 and π, and θ' is <u>either</u> between 0 and π <u>or else</u> between π and 2π. Similarly, if $\pi < \theta < 2\pi$, then <u>either</u> $\pi < \theta' < 2\pi$ <u>or else</u> $0 < \theta' < \pi$. We can prove that in each case the first alternative for θ' is correct and the second alternative is false, as follows.

Consider a particular ¹int A_1 and re-gard $A_1 0'$ in Fig. A as playing the role of MN in Fig. B on page 22. 0 plays the role of the roaming point X in Fig. B, where now 0, instead of varying along a curve that includes neither M nor N, will vary along

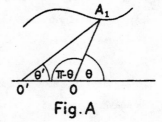

Fig. A

straight line $\underline{l}$ and so will coincide eventually with $0'$. We know that θ, $\pi - \theta$ *, and θ' all vary continuously; the first two between 0 and π, and θ' either between 0 and π or between π and 2π. But since θ can be momentarily equal to θ', θ' must have at least one value between 0 and π and so cannot have any value between π and 2π. Thus θ', vary-ing continuously, must always have values between 0 and π when θ has values between 0 and π.

Similarly, if we consider any point A_2, we have $\pi < \theta < 2\pi$ and $\pi < \theta' < 2\pi$.

This means that the separation of points A into classes A_1 and A_2 with respect to 0 is unaltered when the separation is made with respect to any other point $0'$ on $\underline{l}$. That is, all the points on $\underline{l}$, and so $\underline{l}$ itself, sep-arate the points A that are not on $\underline{l}$ into two classes in the same way. The points of one class are said to be <u>on one side</u> of line $\underline{l}$; the points of the other class are said to be <u>on the other side</u> of line $\underline{l}$.

<u>Fundamental Theorem</u> 2. A straight line joining points A_1 and A_2, on opposite sides of line $\underline{l}$, must have a point in common with $\underline{l}$.

——————
*i.e., angle MXN in Fig. B on page 22.

- 23 -

Proof: Consider a random point O on line
$\underline{l}$. See Fig. A. Let O vary along line $\underline{l}$. As
it does so, angle A_1OA_2 will vary continu-
ously, since it plays the role of angle MXN
in Fig. B on page 22. This angle A_1OA_2, or
$\theta_2 - \theta_1$, will vary continuously from 0^+ radians (when O is way out to the right) to
$2\pi^-$ radians (when O is way out to the left).

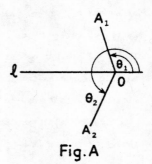

Fig. A

Consequently for some position of O the value of $\angle A_1OA_2$ will be π radians and A_1OA_2 will be a straight line having point O in common with $\underline{l}$.

Fundamental Theorem 3. ("Pasch's Axiom") Through any point P on one
side AB of triangle ABC, every line $\underline{l}$ that does not contain a vertex has
a point in common with either BC or AC. See Fig. B.

Proof: Angle BPC is between O and π; also,
the given line $\underline{l}$ contains a half-line with end-
point P that makes with side AB an angle ϕ different from $\angle$ BPC and such that $0 < \phi < \pi$.
Let point Q trace out the broken line BCA so that
angle BPQ varies continuously from O to π. For

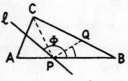

Fig. B

some position of Q angle BPQ is equal to ϕ, and Q is the intersection
of $\underline{l}$ and the broken line BCA.

Fundamental Theorem 4. A line joining a point inside a circle and
a point outside a circle must have a point in common with the circle.

Proof: If, in Fig. C, P is inside the circle and Q is outside, then -
from the definitions of "circle," "inside," and
"outside" on page 133 - it follows that OP < r. Let
D be the foot of the perpendicular from O to the
line $\underline{l}$ joining P and Q. Then OD $\leq$ OP < r and
$\sqrt{r^2 - \overline{OD}^2}$ < r. We can lay off this distance

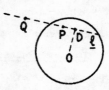

Fig. C

- 24 -

$\sqrt{r^2 - \overline{OD}^2}$ on $\underline{l}$ in two directions from D and thus determine two points on $\underline{l}$ that are at a distance r from 0. These two points will also be on the circle. See page 138.

Fundamental Theorem 5. A circular arc $\underline{b}$ joining a point inside a circle $\underline{a}$ to a point outside circle $\underline{a}$ must have a point in common with circle $\underline{a}$.

Proof: Given P inside and Q outside the cir-
cular arc $\underline{a}$ with center 0 and joined by the circular arc $\underline{b}$ with center 0', we see that OP < r
and O'P = r'. Consequently OO' must be less than
r + r' and we have the case of two circles intersecting in two points as shown on pages 142 and 143.

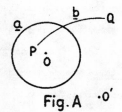

Fig. A

Returning to Theorems A, B, and C, pages 21-23, we see that the Principle of Angle Measure, amplified as on page 231, suffices to establish
the unique bisector of angle A and to insure that this bisector meets BC
between B and C. For as X varies continuously from
B to C in Fig. B, angle BAX varies continuously from
0 to $\angle$ BAC, and vice versa. Corresponding to the
unique number that is half the sum of the numbers
assigned to the points B and C there is a unique number that lies between the numbers assigned to the
half-lines AB and AC. And vice versa, corresponding
to the unique number that is half the sum of the numbers assigned to the
half-lines AB and AC there is a unique number that lies between the numbers assigned to the points B and C. It is the object of Theorems C and
B respectively to prove in effect that this "unique number that lies
between - - -" lies just midway between. Even in the main part of this
geometry, however, we do not intend to make such conspicuous use of number in discussing or proving theorems. For the most part we shall be

Fig. B

content in the knowledge that the system of real numbers is back of us
to help us whenever we may be challenged.

All that is expected of the pupil with respect to Theorems B and C
is that he shall see for himself that enough parts of two triangles are
given equal, or can easily be proved to be equal, to enable him to prove
that the triangles are equal. For the teacher to lead the pupil by hint
or suggestion to the gist of the proof and then stress the form of the
proof that the pupils must use is quite the opposite of what the authors
desire. They much prefer that the pupils see the relations between these
three theorems than that they use them as dress rehearsal for a new bit
of verbal gymnastics. The chief aim of the authors with respect to the
three assumptions on page 20, the three theorems A, B, C, and the further
theorems suggested by Exs. 1-4 on page 24 is that the pupil shall see
them as a whole and shall recognize that these propositions, together
with certain undefined and defined terms, constitute by themselves a
miniature geometry. This is mentioned on page 25 of the book and is
there related to the main system of geometry in this book that begins in
Chapter 2.

Pages 24-25: Exercises.

1. Certain teachers will insist that lines PA and PB ought to be shown
   in Fig. 5, and that they ought to be full lines and not dotted, in
   order to conform to a convention that given and required lines, or
   lengths, shall be shown as full lines. The authors do not oppose
   this convention whenever it coincides with their larger aims, but
   they do not intend to be bound by it whenever they think that the interests of the pupils can be better served by ignoring it. Often
   this convention requires that the book show lines that are essential
   to the proof but are better withheld till the pupil sees the need of
   them. In such cases the authors prefer to have the pupil supply the

- 26 -

necessary lines on his own diagram. Sometimes also the authors choose
to emphasize the crucial lines of a configuration by suppressing lines
of secondary importance. They regard the discovery and appreciation
of geometric relations, and of logical relations, as more important
to the pupil than the preservation of certain conventional procedures.

2. The word "theorem" is not to be interpreted as meaning only general
propositions. The definition of "theorem" on page 19 is broad enough
to include propositions that are stated in terms of a particular
figure.

Do not suggest the theorem and its proof. We want pupils to see
problems as well as to solve problems proposed by other people. It
would be good to tell the pupils precisely this and to anticipate a
good response. We must train pupils to look for relations and not
encourage them to wait till the relations are handed to them.

In Exs. 2 and 3 they are expected to see and prove two of the following three theorems: (1) that $\angle ABD = \angle ACD$, by Theorem A; (2) that
AD, when drawn, will bisect $\angle BAC$, by Assumption 1; and (3) that AD
will bisect BC, by Theorem B.

4. The pupil may suggest several relations between the angles of this
figure that are true, but they all involve the relation $\angle A = \angle D$, so
this must be proved in any case. Some pupils will suggest that triangles BAC and BDC are equal. They may even say that whenever three
sides of one triangle are equal to the three sides of a second triangle, the triangles are equal. That is, they may even announce a
general theorem, one that is independent of the particular diagram
shown in Fig. 7.

These first four exercises are well within the powers of pupils in
the junior high school even. The authors believe that this sort of
exercise is easier and more significant than the traditional reciting

- 27 -

of proofs of the first two congruence theorems and of the dreary pronouncement that vertical angles are equal. They wish their attitude to be interpreted as "giving the game back to the students."

6. (a) In a circle, if chords are equal, then the chords are equally distant from the center of the circle.

(b) If a quadrilateral is a parallelogram, then the opposite angles of the quadrilateral are equal.

(c) If a baby is hungry, then the baby cries.

Page 25, last line. The authors wish to begin using the word "demonstration" at this point but know of no definition that would not be psychologically ridiculous. Consequently they have introduced the word with no explanation except as may be gathered from the series of examples of demonstration on the immediately preceding pages. Much of our mother tongue is learned from encounters of just this sort, with nothing but the context to suggest the meaning.

Page 26: Converse propositions.* The teacher should note that a proposition is almost never stated in such a form that the converse can be written down merely by literally interchanging hypothesis and conclusion. Consider, for example, the proposition "If two oblique lines are drawn from a point to a line, the more remote is the greater." In our comment on page 22 of the book (page 17 in this manual) we have called attention to the fact that the "universe of discourse" is ordinarily mentioned in either the hypothesis or the conclusion. Sometimes it is mentioned in neither, but it is always implicit in both. So long as it

_____
*The teacher will find much instruction in the series of articles by Nathan Lazar entitled "The Importance of Certain Concepts and Laws of Logic for the Study and Teaching of Geometry" that appeared in the Mathematics Teacher, Vol. XXXI nos. 3-5, March-May, 1938. We hope, however, that the complexities of this subject as set forth by Dr. Lazar will not dissuade the teacher from discussing converses in full at a more elementary level with his pupils. The treatment of converses in this manual is intended to show the teacher how to introduce beginners to this subject without overwhelming them with details that interest adults.

is rhetorically a part of either the hypothesis or conclusion of a proposition, but not of both, the proposition that is ordinarily recognized by mathematicians as the converse of the given proposition is strictly a partial converse, the universe of discourse being kept as part of the new hypothesis (conclusion) instead of being made a part of the new conclusion (hypothesis). It is possible, however, always to separate out the universe of discourse linguistically from the if-part and the then-part. When that is done, the converse proposition is correctly given by a complete interchange of hypothesis and conclusion. For example, in the proposition just mentioned above, the two oblique lines are not explicitly mentioned in the conclusion, although implied by the words "more" and "greater." The perpendicular from the point to the line is not mentioned in either the hypothesis or the conclusion, although implied by the word "remote" and possibly also by the word "oblique." The universe of discourse in this proposition can be separated out by writing the proposition in the following form: "Given the perpendicular and two oblique lines from a point to a line; if one oblique line is more remote than the other, it is greater than the other." The converse is "Given the perpendicular and two oblique lines from a point to a line; if one oblique line is greater than the other, it is more remote than the other."

If books on geometry always took pains to write their propositions so that a literal interchange of this sort would yield the converse, there would still be the problem of training pupils to frame the converses of non-mathematical propositions, where the separation of hypothesis and conclusion calls for considerable discrimination. The pupils might as well face this problem in geometry, particularly since a studied effort to avoid it would result in very stilted statements of many theorems.

The discussion in the text on pages 26 and 27 is intended to be sufficiently broad to rule out the necessity of mentioning so-called "partial converses." For while it is possible to regard the wording of certain propositions in such a way that the hypothesis, or the conclusion, or both, shall seem to have more than one part; and while it is possible then to devise all the partial converses that can result from interchanging one or more of these partial hypotheses and conclusions, it is neither necessary nor desirable to do this. If we will avoid a too literal interpretation of hypothesis and conclusion, and will first set at one side those ideas in the proposition that are obviously intended to be considered as invariant, then it is possible to frame the converse without raising the question of partial converses at all. As we shall see two paragraphs farther on, a proposition can be so worded that it has more than one meaning, although the person who wrote it intended that it should have only one. In such cases it is necessary first to guess the writer's intent. Admittedly it requires a modicum of common sense to do this, and some agreement as to what is common sense in a given case; but it seems better in writing converses to rely charitably on a bit of "I know what you mean" and "you know what I mean" than to lose ourselves in the alternative of a maze of partial converses.

It may seem preposterous to some that we insist regularly on correct thinking and accurate expression and then advocate this apparently lackadaisical treatment of converses. Actually our interest in precise thought and expression is unabated. But we must bear in mind that the inconsistencies and colloquialisms of the English language make it a difficult and unnatural vehicle for sustained orderly expression of logically connected ideas. This is true of other living languages also, and explains why those who write on logic and on the foundations of mathematics employ some form of the artificial Peano notation that was devised for this special purpose. So long as we continue to use English in our mathematics classes, we shall have to forego the complete accuracy of expression that

we should like to demand of our pupils - and of ourselves. A reasonable
relaxation in the face of necessity need not imply - and surely does not
imply in this instance - an abandonment of standards in general. We
shall still demand all the accuracy that the pupil can fairly be expected
to deliver.

Consider, for example, the proposition "In an isosceles triangle the
bisector of the vertex angle bisects the base." (Defined on page 245.)
It is possible to think of the triangle idea as alone invariant here.
In that case there will be three parts to the hypothesis: (1) the isosceles idea, (2) the line-through-vertex idea, and (3) the idea that this
line bisects the vertex angle; and there will be two parts to the conclusion: (1) the line through the vertex meets the base, and (2) this
line bisects the base. It is then possible to regard as a partial converse of the original proposition any rewording that interchanges one or
more parts of the hypothesis with an equal number of parts of the conclusion. This will yield nine partial converses in all; six by interchanging one part of the hypothesis with one part of the conclusion in
all possible ways, and three by interchanging two parts of the hypothesis
with two parts of the conclusion in all possible ways. Of these nine,
five are true and four are false. Of the five partial converses that
are true, one is utterly trivial; one differs in only a trivial way from
the original proposition; one is the converse that we regard as "the real
converse"; and the last two state essentially that if the bisector of the
vertex angle bisects the base, then the triangle is isosceles. This has
an interesting proof, involving the so-called ambiguous case. (See pages
186-188 of BASIC GEOMETRY.) It appears at first that the base angles can
be either equal or supplementary. The latter alternative is then dis-
missed as impossible because it requires two sides of the triangle to be
parallel. The content of this proposition is as interesting as its proof;

but it is not what we should ordinarily regard as a converse of the original proposition unless, in reading the proposition, we give unusual
stress to the word "isosceles."

Now all this seems pretty far-fetched. The statement of the original
proposition clearly limits the possible situations to those involving an
isosceles triangle; so both the triangle idea and the isosceles idea
ought to be regarded as invariant. If then we think of the number of
parts of the hypothesis as being reduced to two, while the conclusion
keeps its two parts as before, we have the possibility of five partial
converses: four by interchanging one part of the hypothesis with one part
of the conclusion in all possible ways, and one by interchanging both
parts of the hypothesis with both parts of the conclusion. Of these
five, three are true and two are false; of the three that are true, one
is utterly trivial and another differs in only a trivial way from the
original proposition. The third is the only one that tells us anything
new; and this is the one that we should ordinarily regard as the converse
of the given proposition.

By keeping the isosceles idea invariant we have reduced the number of
partial converses that must be considered; but we must still pay a considerable price in false and trivial propositions if we go about the de-
termination of converses in this manner. It is evident that the singling
out of the ideas that the line in question shall go through the vertex
and that it shall also meet the base yields nothing of significance and
serves only to add annoying complexity to an otherwise simple procedure.
If then we refuse to regard the wording of the original proposition as
inviting consideration of the possibility that the line in question
avoids the vertex, or that it does not meet the base, then we have left
only one part in the hypothesis and only one part in the conclusion; and

the interchange of these yields the only converse that - from the pupil's point of view - can reasonably be ascribed to the original proposition.

In short, if one will read the statement of a proposition charitably, it is not hard to decide how the converse should be stated. It is quite unnecessary to introduce difficulties here that can be resolved only by the consideration of partial converses. True, there are a few propositions that are commonly worded in such a way as seemingly to invite the introduction of partial converses. It is possible, however, to reword these propositions so as to remove this invitation; and that is a much simpler procedure than helplessly to leave the traditional wording unaltered and expose oneself needlessly to all the rigmarole of partial converses.

For example, one could say "Given two triangles in which two sides of one are respectively equal to two sides of the other; if the included angle in the first triangle is greater than the included angle in the second triangle, then the third side of the first triangle is greater than the third side of the second triangle." This is not as clear as the usual wording, and requires a charitable interpretation of the word "included." But the content of the converse is unmistakable, whatever may be charged against the way it is worded. After all, every use of English in mathematical situations requires some leniency in interpretation. In the case just noted it would seem better to keep the smoother traditional wording and to rely on "You know what I mean" when citing the converse; for the difficulty here is linguistic rather than logical. But we have indicated a way out for those who wish to avoid challenge with respect to partial converses.

Page 28: Exercises.

1. Converse is true.   2. Converse is false.

- 33 -

3. Converse is false.   4. Converse is false.

5. Converse is false.   6. Converse is true.

7. Converse is false.   8. Converse is true.

9. Converse is false.   10. Converse is false.

11. Converse is false.

Page 28: "If and only if . . . ." While the authors see no reason to mention the phrase "necessary and sufficient condition" in this connection, since no important use could be made of it in this geometry, it is well for the teacher to recognize that every proposition "If A ..., then B..." can be subjected to two interpretations: A is a sufficient condition for B, and B is a necessary condition for A. For example, in the proposition "If a quadrilateral is a parallelogram, then two opposite sides of the quadrilateral are equal" the fact that the quadrilateral is a parallelogram is a sufficient condition - but not a necessary condition - for the equality of two opposite sides; also, the equality of two opposite sides is a necessary condition - but not a sufficient condition - for the quadrilateral to be a parallelogram; for consider in each case an isosceles trapezoid.

Similarly, in the case of the converse proposition "If B, then A ...," we can say: B is a sufficient condition for A, and A is a necessary condition for B. Consequently, if anyone wishes to establish that A is both a necessary and a sufficient condition for B, he must be able to prove "If B, then A" in addition to "If A, then B." That is, if a proposition and its converse proposition are both true, the hypothesis (conclusion) of either proposition is a necessary and sufficient condition for the conclusion (hypothesis) of this same proposition.

We make no use of these ideas in this book; but if the teacher wishes to use them, he must be warned against the common error of pupils in confusing the colloquial and the scientific uses of the word "necessary."

The pupil is likely to interpret "necessary condition for B" as meaning "If..., then **necessarily** B," which is precisely the opposite of accepted practice among mathematicians. For "If..., then necessarily B" merely intensifies the sufficient condition for B by inserting the word "necessarily."

Pages 30-31: Exercises.

8. In a group as large as the total population of the United States, about fifty per cent would be below average.

9. Or were the Navy and Yale teams stronger than Vernon and Aggie?

Page 32, lines 9, 10. The third step ought to be CD = CD.

Page 33, lines 1-4. See comments on page 280, Exs. 14 and 15, in this manual.

Page 33, lines 9-13 contain two very important ideas for the teacher to emphasize.

Page 33: Indirect Method. "Logically it is just as convincing. Logically yes, but not psychologically. Pupils are always dubious about the propriety of the Indirect Method. This is hinted at on page 35, lines 15-16 of the text. Logically it is indeed true that a proposition can be established by showing that denial of the conclusion leads to denial of the hypothesis. That is, it is logically correct to assert that the proposition "If B is not true, then A is not true" implies the proposition "If A is true, then B is true." For if this second proposition does not follow from the first, then its denial must follow from the first, namely "If A is true, then B is not true"; and so, from the first, A is not true. But it is a fundamental principle underlying the sort of reasoning we use in this book that A cannot be at the same time both true and not true. Consequently the supposition that the second proposition does not follow from the first is untenable. Our reasoning here depends upon two principles that underlie all the reasoning in this book

- 35 -

and all reasoning in everyday life. The first of these principles asserts that every mathematical entity and configuration either possesses a given property or else does not possess it. The second principle asserts that no mathematical entity or configuration can possess both a given property and its opposite. These principles are often applied so as to mean, in effect, that every proposition must be either true or untrue; and that no proposition can be both true and untrue.

It is clear then that the Indirect Method is but an application of the logic underlying all our reasoning. It is clear also that to assert the logical equivalence of the two propositions "If A is true, then B is true" and "If B is not true, then A is not true" is but to assert in other phraseology the validity of the Indirect Method and hence to assert indirectly the validity of a fundamental principle of our logic. These ideas will not appeal, of course, to secondary-school pupils. That is why on page 247 of the text we use the Indirect Method to establish the ideas set forth on that page and do not go back of those ideas as we have just done here.

C H A P T E R 2

Lesson Plan Outline: 15 lessons

1-2. Through page 45, line 7

3-4. Through page 51, Ex. 8

  5. Exs. 9-16, pages 51-52

6-7. Through page 56 (The exercises on page 56 require time for careful consideration.)

  8. Page 57 through Ex. 6 on page 61

  9. Exs. 7-13, pages 61-63

10. Exs. 14, 16-21, pages 63-64

11. Exs. 15, 22-30, pages 63-64

12. Exs. 31-34, page 65

13. Exs. 35-38, page 66

14-15. Pages 68-69

<u>Page 38, line 15</u>: "We shall need only five." See note in this manual, page 6, referring to pages 50, 198, 199, and 222 of the text.

<u>Page 39.</u> The undefined terms on this page do not include the term plane, even though the word "plane" appears on that page, because all the points and lines of this geometry are considered as being restricted to an unmentioned and undescribed domain, as indicated in line 5 and in lines 19 and 20. This domain is referred to for convenience as a plane, but every such reference could be replaced by a circumlocution such as "the class of all points - - -," or the like. If this geometry included three dimensional material "officially," then we should need to list "plane" as an undefined term, or else define it.

<u>Page 39, lines 20-22</u>: "Though it is possible to prove this." This has already been proved in the comments under Chapter 1 in this manual.

<u>Page 40, lines 7-10.</u> These directions are meant to be taken literally by the pupil.

- 37 -

Page 40: Principle 1. Of the five basic principles, nos. 1, 3, and 5 are the most important. They have been given distinctive labels so that they may be conveniently referred to. Principle 1 says in effect, "All the points on a straight line can be numbered so as to serve as a ruler*"; and Principle 3 says in effect, "All half-lines having the same end-point can be numbered so as to serve as a protractor." Notice the duality** between these two principles: all the points having a common line - - -, and all the lines having a common point - - -.

On page 39 the undefined idea of straight line is assumed to include the notion that a straight line is a collection of points. In Principle 1 these points are paired with the elements of some number system that will make an adequate scale for line measure. Neither the system of integers nor the system of rational numbers is adequate for this purpose, for we might sometime wish to measure the diagonal of a unit square, or the like. Consequently Principle 1 implies that the points of a straight line can be paired with the real numbers. This means that the properties of continuity and infinite extensibility of the system of real numbers are to be properties also of any collection of points that constitutes a straight line. Consequently this geometry does not need to state explicitly that it assumes the infinite extensibility of straight lines; or that it assumes the existence of the mid-point, or any other point of division, of a line segment. These ideas are all implied by the intimate association between the system of real numbers and the points of a line that is inherent in Principle 1.

In similar manner the existence of the bisector of an angle is im-

---

*By "ruler" we mean here what the pupil means by "ruler." Eventually in this book we replace this word by the word "scale" and denote an unmarked ruler by the word "straightedge." See Chapter 6, pages 165-166.

**For a discussion of duality see Graustein, W. C., Introduction to Higher Geometry, Macmillan, 1930, or Veblen and Young, Projective Geometry, Vol. I, Ginn, 1910.

plied by Principle 3, the Principle of Angle Measure, as stated on page 47. Consequently, BASIC GEOMETRY is not troubled by the question of "hypothetical constructions" that plagues other geometries. When we set out to prove the first theorem that involves the bisector of an angle, we do not need to puzzle over the problem of how to demonstrate the constructibility of the bisector without making use of the theorem we wish to prove, or - foiled in that - to satisfy our consciences that it will be all right to prove the theorem first and demonstrate the existence of the bisector later. For our Principle of Angle Measure tells us that in the case of any angle we can always find the number that is midway between the numbers assigned to the sides of the angle. In this geometry, therefore, it is no impropriety to postpone all discussion of constructions until Chapter 6.

There are probably other instances in BASIC GEOMETRY where a traditional logical loophole will seem to be still unplugged and where teachers will say of the authors, "Ah, they've missed that one, too!" In most of these cases, however, the real number system, our ever present help in time of trouble, will come to our defense. What counts as truly an omission or an oversight in other systems of geometry may seem to be an omission or an oversight in this geometry also, whereas actually it has been cared for under some aspect of the system of real numbers. Either the seemingly unmentioned assumptions of this geometry are really mentioned but are not recognized as being mentioned because of this unusual tie-up with real numbers; or else they are not assumptions at all, but - like the five theorems considered in our comments on Theorem A in Chapter 1 - are direct, but unmentioned, consequences of more fundamental statements in this geometry. There is more meaning packed into the last paragraph of page 4 of the Preface of BASIC GEOMETRY than most teachers will appreciate until they have poked around a bit in the cellar of this

geometry. Nevertheless, despite our great care to build a firm foundation where others before us have left a crack or two, it is too much to
expect that we have not erred somewhere, either positively or by omission.

Surely we have not set down in the text a clear statement of all the
properties bestowed upon straight line and angle by associating the system of real numbers with them. It is our opinion that explicit mention
of these details would confuse the pupils. We have preferred, therefore,
to let these details stand as tacit implications of the Principles of
Line Measure and of Angle Measure. To some extent it is a matter of
judgment as to how many of the horrid details one can reveal without
overwhelming the student. We make a clean breast of the matter here in
this manual for teachers and leave the final decision to them. That is
what this manual is for.

Page 40, line 17: Units of length. The implication here is that
"a unit" is "an inch" or "a centimeter" or the like; that is, "1 inch"
or "1 centimeter."

Pages 41-42: Exercises. If in this geometry we were going to employ
signed numbers, directed distances (pages 42-43), and directed angles
(page 49), we should make more of the idea that is barely hinted at in
Ex. 1. This idea comes to the surface momentarily in the Review Exercises on page 68, but we cannot do more with it without making the proofs
throughout this geometry too fussy. For the most part we shall use un-
signed numbers. Birkhoff's treatment of this geometry in the Annals of
Mathematics uses directed distances and angles, but it is clear that
that treatment is too difficult for secondary school pupils. Nevertheless the authors have felt bound in BASIC GEOMETRY to mention directed
distances and directed angles briefly, even though they dismiss the idea
immediately, because it adds to the pupil's appreciation of the difficulties attendant upon the measurement of angles if he considers, even
momentarily, how signed numbers can be used to distinguish the four di-

rected angles of less than 360° that are formed by two distinct half-lines having a common endpoint. (See page 235 of BASIC GEOMETRY, and the comment farther along in this chapter of the manual on Angle(s).)

In Exs. 5 and 6, 137 centimeters and 160 centimeters are roughly equivalent to 54 inches and 63 inches respectively. Perhaps some pupils will observe this. The second parts of these exercises reveal that the ratio of two measures is the same, regardless of the unit that is used.

Page 43, lines 12-18. This idea that there are two and only two distinct points on the line at a distance d from Q will prove very helpful later when we discuss the intersection of straight line and circle, page 138, and the intersection of two circles, page 142.

Page 43: Notion of Betweenness. Some of the logical loopholes in Euclid's Elements are traceable to his failure to mention explicitly certain ideas concerning the order of the points on a line, and the order of lines (or half-lines) having a common point; ideas which undoubtedly he would have accepted as a matter of course. In this geometry we use the ideas of order inherent in the system of real numbers (see Postulates 18-20 on page 287) to establish the order of points on a line and the order of lines through a point. Defining "betweenness" in terms of order - for numbers on page 287, for points on a line on page 43, and for lines through a point on pages 53 and 54 - we have the means of defining "line-segment," "bisect," and "mid-point" on page 44, "bisector of angle" on page 48, and "arc of a circle" on page 134. These latter definitions all stem from the system of real numbers.

Page 44: Principle 2. Teachers will be interested to note here the duality between the ideas "not more than one straight line through two given points" and "not more than one point common to two given straight lines"; to note also the breakdown of this duality when "not more than one" is replaced by "at least one."

Page 45: Half-line. The authors have preferred to use the term

- 41 -

"half-line" instead of "ray" for two reasons: its relation to the parent endless line is more clearly indicated by "half-line" than by "ray"; and neither term is so commonly used in elementary geometry that the displacing of one by the other is of any great moment. The teacher will note that it is also possible to divide an endless straight line into two parts such that one part contains P and all points whose numbers are greater than p, and the other part contains all the points whose numbers are less than p. But we do not call this latter part a half-line. The definition of half-line demands that it have an end-point. The phrase "divides the straight line into two half-lines" is not to be understood in the sense that two halves make a whole, because the point P must do double duty, serving as end-point of each half-line.

The pupil may be puzzled also by the statement that the point P may be selected anywhere on the endless straight line. He must abandon any idea he may have had that P is the mid-point of this line, for the term "mid-point" is defined on page 44 of BASIC GEOMETRY - as in other elementary geometries - with respect to line-segments only.

These difficulties are inherent in the concept "endless straight line" and are not peculiar to BASIC GEOMETRY or to the word "half-line." It is quite natural that we should try to apply the familiar rules of finite arithmetic to the arithmetic of infinite numbers and should try to transfer the ideas associated with ended line-segments to situations involving endless straight lines. Nevertheless, we have no right to do so. Let the pupil consider the difference between the finite assemblages 1, 2, 3, 4, 5, 6 and 2, 4, 6 and the infinite assemblages 1, 2, 3, 4, 5, 6, ... and 2, 4, 6, ... The second finite assemblage contains half as many integers as the first; but there is the same number of integers in both infinite assemblages. For all the integers in the second infinite assemblage can be paired with all the integers in the first, and this - by definition - is what we mean by "the same number" in the arithmetic of finite and of infinite numbers.

The ideas of infinite numbers and of infinite assemblages of points are far removed from everyday life. Nevertheless they are necessary and fundamental to our adult thinking about elementary arithmetic and geometry. Because they are fundamental they may arise in class discussions at the very beginning of geometry. There is no way of avoiding them in any discussion of geometry that aims to open the pupil's eyes to things as they are. Similarly, any pupil in an arithmetic class who inquires why the decimal equivalents of certain fractions contain only a few digits, while others like $\frac{1}{3}$ and $\frac{2}{7}$ have decimal equivalents that "go on forever," endlessly repeating a digit or a group of digits, can be answered only by reference to the infinite divisibility of finite quantities.

Actually the points of a half-line, omitting the end-point, can be paired with all the points of an endless straight line. For all the points except A of half-line $\underline{l}$ in Fig. A can be paired, by central projection, with all the points except the endpoints A and B of the quadrant AB; this quadrant can then be altered to the semi-circle A'B', without end-points, of half the radius of quadrant AB;* and all the points of this semi-circle, omitting A' and B', can be paired with all the points of the endless straight line $\underline{m}$. Consequently a halfline, including its end-point, contains one more point than an endless straight line! Evidently the familiar statement concerning finite quantities "The whole is greater than any

Fig. A

----

*This can be done by a parallel projection that carries every point except O and B of the radius OB into some point between A' and B' of diameter A'B'. This will pair every point except A and B of the quadrant with every point between A' and B' of the semi-circle.

of its parts and equal to the sum of them" is not applicable to infinite quantities.

Page 46: Angle(s). It will be noted that in this geometry "angle" is an undefined term. If this undefined term connotes - as it does to most people - a concept that is unique, then the configuration shown in Fig. 5 is highly ambiguous. For this configuration shows two angles AVB of less than 360 degrees in absolute value and indefinitely many more of more than 360 degrees. A possible alternative is to bind up all this ambiguity in the connotation of the undefined term itself, so that it shall mean all possible angles AVB to all people. A partial paraphrase of Birkhoff's treatment of angle in his article in the Annals exhibits this alternative as follows: "The half-lines l, m, - - - through any point V can be put into one-to-one correspondence with the real numbers a, modulo 360, so that, if A (different from V) and B (different from V) are points of l and m respectively, the difference $a_m - a_l$, modulo 360, is $\angle AVB$." After adding an important note concerning continuity and linking $\angle AVB$ with $\angle lVm$, he goes on to say, "It will

Fig. A

be seen that the angle $\angle lVm$ as here conceived is the directed angle from the half-line l to the half-line m determining the position of m relative to l. The ordinary sensed angle of the usual type is obtained by taking some single algebraic difference $a_m - a_l$ which is thought of as representative of an angle generated by the continuous rotation of a half-line from l to m. The ordinary angle $\angle lVm$ is then given by the numerical value of the least residue of $a_m - a_l$, modulo 360." The meaning of this terminology is explained in the next paragraph for those who are not familiar with it.

Linking the half-line l with the real numbers a, modulo 360, means that if half-line l has the number 50, it has the numbers $50 \pm n \cdot 360$,

- 44 -

where n = 0, ± 1, ± 2, - - - -. Similarly for the half-line $\underline{m}$. Consequently the difference $\underline{a}_m - \underline{a}_l$ yields an infinite set of numbers having the same residue (in absolute value) when divided by 360. Each of these algebraic differences corresponds to an "ordinary sensed angle of the usual type." Thus if half-line $\underline{m}$ has the number $470 \pm n \cdot 360$, some of the ordinary sensed angles $\angle \mathrm{1Vm}$ are 420, 60, -300, and the ordinary angle $\angle \mathrm{1Vm}$ is 60, which is the least residue. This "least residue" is that one of this set whose absolute value is less than 180. Of the infinite set of ordinary sensed angles - - - -, 590, 230, -130, -490, - - - - the ordinary angle is 130, being that one of this set whose absolute value is less than 180.

This complexity with respect to sensed angles explains why in BASIC GEOMETRY we have chosen to deal with ordinary angles almost entirely. On page 235 we have introduced directed angles that are limited for the most part to angles between +360 and -360. Removing this restriction and admitting the general sensed angle introduces further complications that would overwhelm a pupil in his first month of demonstrative geometry. To incorporate in the undefined term "angle" the multiple ambiguities that so easily associate themselves with this term, and then, in keeping with this idea, to define angle measure so as to embrace the general directed angle, is the mathematician's way of bringing order to this chaotic topic. But the beginner, who ordinarily sees no complications of this sort, does better to associate with the undefined term "angle" a connotation implying that an angle is unique. This is the connotation of angle that he has gradually acquired in his previous schooling and we do well not to upset it at this time. That is why the text says (page 46, lines 1-3) that two half-lines having the same end-point form two angles

The footnote on page 46 refers to a method of distinguishing these two angles AVB by means of the idea of betweenness. One way of doing

- 45 -

this is to consider all points of the straight line r
through A and B as being numbered, and all the half-
lines having endpoint V as being numbered. One of
the angles AVB can be distinguished from the other
by the property that some, or no, half-line between
the sides of the angle* intersects line r in a point bearing a number
between a and b.

In the special case of straight angles, about to be considered, this
line r must be drawn so as to intersect VA obliquely. The two angles
AVB can then be distinguished by the property that some, or no, half-line
between the sides of the angle intersects line r in a point bearing a
number less than a.

One important reason for considering straight-angles is that they
afford a way of establishing a unit of angle-measure, as on page 50.

Pages 47-49: Principle 3. The comments pertinent to this section
on angle measure have been given already in this chapter in other con-
nections.

The second paragraph of the footnote on page 47 refers to an ambiguity in usage that has a parallel in our ambiguous use of the terms "altitude," "diameter," and so forth, to denote line-segments and also their
lengths.

Page 50: Principle 4. Actually Principle 4 is a theorem that can be
proved by the aid of Principle 5. The proof is in two parts. We first
prove that if l and m are two half-lines of a single straight line n,
then ∠10m is a straight angle. Second, we prove that if the half-lines
l and m meet at O to form a straight angle, the two half-lines are "corresponding halves" of the same straight line. By this proof of theorem
and converse we identify every straight angle with a straight line.

---

*i.e., bearing a number that is between the numbers assigned to the
sides of the angle.

Part 1. Given straight line n with point O and corresponding half-lines l and m. Choose A in l and B in m so that OA = OB. In the degenerate triangles OAB and OBA we have OA = OB, AB = BA, and positive (counter-clockwise) ∠ OAB = positive (counter-clockwise) ∠ OBA.

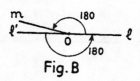

Fig. A

By Principle 5, for sensed angles, we have positive (counter-clockwise) ∠ BOA = positive (counter-clockwise) ∠ AOB. But positive ∠ BOA = negative ∠ AOB. Therefore ∠ AOB = - ∠ AOB and 2∠ AOB = 0, modulo 360. It follows that ∠ AOB is either 0 or 180, modulo 360. If ∠ AOB were 0, OA and OB would have to coincide; and this is impossible because A and B were chosen on distinct half-lines. So ∠ AOB is 180, a straight angle.

Part 2. Given half-lines l and m meeting at O to form a straight angle, 180. The other half-line l' with end-point O in the same straight line as l also forms a straight angle with l, by Part I.

Therefore ∠ lOm = 180

∠ l'Ol = 180

and ∠ l'Ol + ∠ lOm = 360, modulo 360, = 0.

But ∠ l'Ol + ∠ lOm = ∠ l'Om (see page 48, line 4). Therefore ∠ l'Om = 360, modulo 360, = 0, and m and l' coincide. So l and m are corresponding halves of the same straight line.

Pages 50 and 54: Perpendicular lines. On the lower half of page 50 it is shown that if two lines intersect so that the angle between two of their half-lines is 90°, this 90° relation is true of three other angles formed at this intersection. Principle 3 insures that through a point O of a given line there exists a half-line such that one of the angles formed at O will be 90°. It insures also, as pointed out on page 54, that there are only two ways in which this half-line can appear, following by analogy the (q - d) and (q + d) reasoning on page 43. This establishes the uniqueness of the perpendicular to a line at a given point of the line. That is, there is one and only one such perpendicular.

- 47 -

Pages 51-52: Exercises.

1. Half-line OM' will be numbered 270. Therefore ∠L'OM' = 270 - 180, and ∠M'OL = 360 - 270.

3-5. One minute of time corresponds to six degrees.

7. 45 + 180, or 225. (Or 225 $\pm$ n·360)

8. r + 180 or r - 180. (The "in general" refers to the random number $\underline{r}$ and not to the generalized notation $\underline{r}$ + 180 $\pm$ n·360, though the latter is the perfect answer, of course.)

9. 132, 180, 312

10. a + r, a + 180, a + r + 180

12. 180° - s°, s°, 180° - s°

15. ∠AVC + ∠CVB = 180°. ½∠AVC + ½∠CVB = 90° is sufficient. Or else, using the numbering in the answer to Ex. 10, the bisectors will be numbered $\frac{a + a + r}{2}$ and $\frac{a + r + a + 180}{2}$, and the difference between these numbers is 90.

Page 52: Units of angle measure. For further discussion of the history of counting and of measurement see David Eugene Smith, History of Mathematics, Vol. I, 1923, Ginn.

Page 55: Polygon. The definition of "polygon" is intentionally so worded as to include polygons like those shown in Fig. A, but we cannot consider the angles of such polygons without using directed angles. We might do something with this idea near the end of the book, say on page 235, if it were considered desirable. The last paragraph on page 55 is intended to rule out cross polygons and, ordinarily, all polygons with re-entrant angles. Consequently the authors felt justified in defining "angle of polygon" higher up on page 55 so as

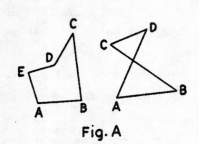

Fig. A

to apply only to convex polygons, building up the idea inductively from the reference to Fig. 18.

Page 56: Exercises. There are only five of these exercises but plenty of time should be allowed for the pupil to make careful drawings and measurements and to absorb the important ideas here.

1. In order to lay off angle CDE properly with the protractor the pupil will need to extend CD.

2. EA = $1\frac{5}{8}$ in. (approx.) $\angle$ DEA = $100°$ (approx.) $\angle$ EAB = $99°$ (approx.) The pupil should be permitted an error of $1°$.

3. CA = 9.0 cm. $\angle$ BCA = $52°$. $\angle$ CAB = $59°$. Sum = $181°$. Many pupils will have an error of at least $1°$ in the sum.

4. A convenient scale is $\frac{1}{2}$ inch or 1 cm. to the mile. The pupil's second angle will be $64°$ clockwise; his third angle $86°$ counter-clockwise; his fourth angle $57°$ clockwise; his fifth angle $53°$ clockwise; his sixth angle $58°$ counter-clockwise. The traveler is approximately 14.6 miles from his starting-point. Direction from start to finish is E$11°$N, approximately.

5. The pupil will need to construct angles of $22°$, $70°$, and $22°$. The vessel sails 15 + 8 + $6\frac{1}{4}$, or $29\frac{1}{4}$ miles.

Page 57: Similarity and proportion. The ideas of correspondence between point and number and of correspondence between angle and number are fundamental in this geometry. The words "corresponding" and "correspondence" are equally fundamental; they are taken as undefined, following the spirit of page 14, lines 18-19, of BASIC GEOMETRY. We do not wish to limit the phrase "corresponding sides of two triangles" to "sides opposite equal angles" in these triangles, because it is often possible to consider two triangles

Fig. A

- 49 -

that are related like those shown in Fig. A on page 49 of this manual, in which the vertices, sides, and angles correspond in pairs despite the absence of equality. In short, Euclidean geometry can be regarded as a special case of projective geometry. The term "correspond" defies definition for beginners, but everyone knows what it means.

The word "proportion" is explained here but is not precisely defined. The definition is assumed from arithmetic. The meaning of proportion is easily grasped; but the definition is more difficult because it involves the word "ratio," which seems to bother pupils. It is for this reason in part that the authors have preferred to use the term "factor of proportionality" rather than "ratio of similitude." The former has the advantage also of being purely numerical, which is what we want; the latter seems to be a number that is necessarily linked with the geometric idea of similarity; and this geometry is based on number even more than it is based on the idea of similarity. The idea of proportion is bigger than any of its applications.

As noted on page 58 of BASIC GEOMETRY, the factor of proportionality k can be any real number, rational or irrational (see page 287). Since we shall not use directed distances in proving theorems we shall make no use of negative values of k; and zero is a limiting case that we do not need to consider.

Section 21 under the Laws of Number (page 287) implies the existence of real numbers that are not rational. For if we should think of the real numbers as being merely the rational numbers under another name, our dream would be rudely shattered by section 21, since there are an infinite number of ways of separating the totality of ordered rationals as therein prescribed without determining a rational s that effects the division. For example, separating the totality of ordered rationals so that C_1 contains all the rationals whose squares are less than $\frac{7}{3}$ and C_2

contains all the rationals whose squares are not less than $\frac{7}{3}$, produces no rational that effects this separation. This sort of separation of the totality of ordered rationals, described in general terms, can serve as the definition of irrational numbers. This is the definition of irrationals referred to on page 4 of the Preface. It follows that if the postulate in section 21 is to hold true, irrationals as well as rationals must be present in the system of real numbers.

This being so, every irrational factor of proportionality indicates an incommensurable case. But BASIC GEOMETRY is not disturbed by this, or required to provide exceptional treatment for incommensurable cases, because its acceptance of the real number system puts rational and irrational on an equal footing. The pupil can always imagine k to be a rational number, and probably will do so. But the proofs of the theorems require no alteration to suit one who imagines k to be irrational.

In connection with Principle 5, Case 1 of Similarity, note that the British Report on The Teaching of Geometry in Schools, G. Bell and Sons, London, 1923, suggests that the usual practice of assuming congruence and parallelism and deducing similarity therefrom can profitably be replaced by assumptions concerning congruence and similarity, from which the former parallel postulate is deduced as a theorem. In BASIC GEOMETRY we go even further and telescope the two suggested postulates of the British Report into one postulate of similarity under which congruence - or equality, as we ordinarily prefer to say - appears as a special case. If we were to go on into solid geometry, this special case of equality would be the only case under similarity that would hold in three dimensions and we should need to make special note in that case to restrict the factor of proportionality k to the single value 1. We hint at this in the exercises following Principles 5, 6, 7, and 8.

The phrasing in italics on page 59, lines 7-9, is an adaptation of similar phrasing in the British Report on The Teaching of Geometry, page 35.

We have already discussed in this manual on page 7 the possibility that Principle 6, Case 2 of Similarity, might have been used instead of Case 1 as a basic postulate of this geometry.

Page 60, lines 2-3: "The logical foundation of our geometry is independent of any idea of motion." If the scale and protractor were officially part of this geometry, then the use of these instruments, as implied in Fig. 2 on page 42, would require the ideas of "move" and "fit," and the statement in question would be too sweeping. Actually, however, the scale and protractor are introduced only as pedagogic devices by which the pupil, familiar with these two instruments, may come gradually to appreciate the logical foundation of this geometry, which is indeed independent of instruments and requires only the numbering of all the points on a line and the numbering of all the half-lines having a common end-point. For example, Ex. 3 on page 60 is not logically required by this geometry. It serves merely to fix an implication of Case 1 of Similarity more surely in the pupil's mind.

Pages 60-66: Exercises. On page 40, in Exs. 1 and 3 on page 56, and again on page 60 we are beginning to wean the pupil away from his familiar but untechnical use of the word "ruler" and to direct his attention to the more precise words "straightedge" and "scale." Because of the confusion that is likely to arise if we should try to turn the pupil from his colloquial use of the word ruler and should ask him now to use the word in its technical meaning of straightedge, we shall abandon the term entirely and shall use straightedge and scale instead. See pages 165 and 280.

5. The third side of the second triangle is _not_ _twice_ the third side of the first triangle; the second and third angles of the second

triangle are <u>not</u> <u>equal</u> to the second and third angles respectively of the first triangle.

6. Yes. Instead of numbering the points on a straight line we can number the points on a great circle in order to measure distances on a sphere; and we can measure angles on a sphere by numbering the half-great-circles that have a common end-point. The concept of angle between two half-great-circles, or minor arcs thereof, as the angle between corresponding tangent lines, can be elaborated by the teacher if the pupils seem to demand it. He can point out the relation between the angle between the tangents to two meridians and the angle between two radii of the sphere that are parallel to these tangents.

7. All that is expected by way of proof is that both pairs of triangles of each quadrilateral shall be treated as indicated in the exercise. The pupil is not expected to consider details as to the order or arrangement of the component triangles.

8-12. The informality permitted in Ex. 7 is to be permitted in these exercises also. They are intended to be easy, informing, but not very exciting original exercises based on Case 1 of Similarity. The introduction of formal details that would make these exercises forbidding to the pupils would be psychologically bad and contrary to the authors' plan. Exs. 11 and 12 are usually proved in full in other geometries; but we have dissected these theorems and considered them piecemeal in Exs. 7-10, so the proofs of Exs. 11 and 12 are merely obvious extensions of the preceding exercises.

16. Notice the gradual build-up of the perpendicular-bisector locus in this book as revealed on pages 63, 81, 88-89, 250-251. Notice that all the ideas essential to a locus are given relatively early, but that the use of the word "locus" itself in this connection is withheld until page 250.

17. By no means tell the pupil which three of the four small triangles he is to work with. Let him discover this for himself. Symmetry alone should suggest the proper choice; but in any case the decision is easily made. He will probably take a look at the fourth triangle to see how that differs from the others. This look-see will probably give him a greater appreciation of the proof of Principle 9 when he comes to it.

18. You would need to know that two triangles that have their corresponding sides proportional are similar. That is, you would need Principle 8, Case 3 of Similarity.

20-37. The teacher should consider all these exercises together and note that they establish certain familiar and very important ideas concerning proportion. The content of these exercises is essentially numerical. Hence the treatment is numerical throughout and purposely avoids all reference to "taking a proportion by alternation," or "by composition," or the like.

21. $\frac{2}{3}$

22. 0.2

23. $\frac{n - m}{m}$

24. $\frac{1}{2}$

25. $\frac{1}{2}$

26. Each fraction equals $\frac{2}{1}$.

27. $\frac{AB'}{AB} = \frac{BB'}{AB} + 1$

28. $\frac{5}{3}$

29. $\frac{6}{5}$

30. $\frac{n + m}{m}$

31. The term "reciprocal" may baffle a few pupils at first, but the context here gives them the clue. The authors often like to introduce partially forgotten, or even new, terms in context in this way,

regarding this as a thoroughly natural way for the pupil to acquire
new words and meanings. From the pupil's point of view it is just
plain common sense that if $\frac{2}{3} = \frac{4}{6}$, then $\frac{3}{2} = \frac{6}{4}$. The authors wish
merely to remind the pupil of this; to generalize this fundamental
numerical idea by using a, b, c, and d; and then to attach a convenient phrasing for later reference, making as little fuss over it as
possible. The statement "reciprocals of equal numbers are equal" is
a theorem in the system of real numbers (see page 288). It is essentially this that the pupil is asked to prove in Ex. 31.

34. Take reciprocals and add 1. The point of Exs. 20-36 is stated after
Exs. 34 and 36; namely to provide justification - aptly phrased -
for asserting any proportion that can be derived from a given proportion, and to show the applicability of this to situations involving
triangles.

37. $\dfrac{a + c + e + - - -}{b + d + f + - - -} = \dfrac{k(b + d + f + - - -)}{b + d + f + - - -} = k = \dfrac{a}{b}$

38. An immediate application of Ex. 37.

Page 67: Summary. The summaries at the end of Chapters 2, 3, 4, 5,
and 7 give the logical plan of BASIC GEOMETRY. Each summary serves also
as a rough index of its chapter. These summaries will help teachers who
are familiar with other systems of geometry to keep the pattern of this
geometry in mind. The authors wish the pupils also to be conscious of
the plan of BASIC GEOMETRY as it unfolds before them, and to see the relation of each theorem to other theorems and to the fundamental postulates. The authors hope that in this way - aided by pointed questions
here and there in this book - the pupils will acquire an appreciation of
a logical system and will recognize the applicability of what they have
learned to other logical systems outside the field of geometry.

Pages 68-69: Exercises. To some extent these exercises force the
pupil to reread the chapter to discover certain details that are properly

ignored until now. Even a relatively dull student can find the answers
by rereading the chapter faithfully. Almost everyone will get the right
answers whether or not his imagination is stimulated - as we hope it will
be - to see that the $\overline{AB}$ + $\overline{BC}$ = $\overline{AC}$ relation for directed line-segments
and the corresponding relation for directed angles serve to link this
geometry with the algebra of the secondary school.

1. See page 41.

2. See pages 42 and 43.

3. 1.5; -1.5

4-6. These exercises extend and generalize the ideas of Ex. 1 on page 41.

   4. $(5.1 - 2.7) + (4.2 - 5.1) = 4.2 - 2.7$

   5. $(4.2 - 5.1) + (2.7 - 4.2) = 2.7 - 5.1$

   6. $(2.7 - 5.1) + (4.2 - 2.7) = 4.2 - 5.1$

7-8. See pages 43-44. Line-segment BC consists of the points B and C
     and all the points between them. These points will be numbered from
     4.2 to 5.1. Line-segment BA consists of all points numbered from
     4.2 to 2.7; it may be considered also as consisting of all points
     numbered from 2.7 to 4.2.

9. See page 47.

10. See page 49.

11. This exercise extends and generalizes the ideas of Exs. 1-3 on
     page 48. $(161 - 106) + (37 - 161) = (37 - 106)$

12. $37 \overset{+}{-} 90 + n \cdot 360$

13. About 2 miles S.E. of Toggenburg

15. $\frac{1}{3}$ and $\frac{3}{4}$

C H A P T E R 3

Lesson Plan Outline: 19 lessons

1. Through pages 73-74, Exs. 1-8

2. Exs. 9, 10, 13, 14, page 75; through Exs. 1-2, page 77

3. Page 75, Exs. 11-12, page 78, Exs. 4-6, 8

4. Page 78, Ex. 7; pages 80-81, Exs. 1-6

5. Page 82, Exs. 7-8. Prove Principle 9. Page 84, Ex. 1

6-9. Pages 84-87, Exs. 2-23

10. Principles 10, 11, 12 (excluding converse)

11. Prove converse and corollaries of Principle 12.

12-16. Exercises, pages 95-98

17-19. Exercises, pages 100-103; take some three dimensional ones each time.

The five fundamental assumptions of Chapter 2 and the seven basic theorems of this chapter establish so many fundamental geometric ideas that they are called the twelve "principles" of this geometry. As indicated in the footnote on page 107, the numbering of assumptions, basic theorems, and later theorems is consecutive in this book. The teacher's attention is called to the final paragraph of page 5 in the Preface to BASIC GEOMETRY and to the note on Principle 11 on page 67 of this manual.

The twelve principles lead immediately to the theorems concerning parallel lines and rectangular networks in Chapter 4, from which one could proceed to develop analytic geometry if it were considered wise to do so. The twelve principles lead also to the theorems concerning the circle in Chapter 5. And from Ex. 12 on page 75 we could develop the ideas of area of triangle and of polygon, as outlined on page 222 at the end of Chapter 7. These three major geometric ideas of parallelism, circle, and area are three independent products of this powerful list of twelve principles.

<u>Page 72: Principle 6, Case 2 of Similarity</u>. Although the proof of Principle 6 suggests superposition, the teacher should note that actual superposition is not used. Instead, a third triangle is constructed that is similar to one of the given triangles. The possibility of this construction - or of the existence of this third triangle - is established by the fundamental postulates of this geometry.

Teachers of geometry who have been accustomed to make free use of symbols such as $\therefore$, $\sim$, $\triangle$, and so on will notice that this book uses almost no symbols. The authors indicate on page 285 that they use the four undefined symbols $=$, $<$, $+$, $\times$. They introduce the symbol $>$ on page 34, which can be defined as on page 282; they introduce the symbol $\angle$ on page 21, and the symbol $\triangle$ on page 200. These seven, only two of which are geometric, constitute the entire list of symbols in this book. There are two reasons for minimizing the number of symbols. First, if we wish to encourage transfer of training in logic from geometric to non-geometric fields, we do well to use the language of everyday life and avoid a highly symbolic mode of expression that requires translation when we pass from geometry to other fields. Second, a highly symbolic ritual with respect to geometry is likely to divert attention from the main object of the instruction. If, however, teacher and pupils wish to introduce other symbols in order to save time there is no harm so long as the symbols do not become an obstruction to thinking. Care must be used in introducing a symbol like $\sim$ for similarity, because in BASIC GEOMETRY similar triangles regularly include equal triangles as a special case and the symbol $\sim$, used in other geometries, does not have quite this connotation.

<u>Pages 73-75: Exercises</u>.

4. The reason for specifying a particular triangle to be enlarged, rather than letting the pupil choose his own triangle, is to prevent

his beginning with an isosceles triangle, or right triangle, or other special case. An excellent supplementary exercise would be to let the pupil choose the first triangle himself but to insist that it be not a special case.

5. 2a

7. $\frac{17}{24}$ x 5 feet, or 3 ft. $6\frac{1}{2}$ in.

8. The pupil is asked to suggest what the foreman on the job would do right on the ground, literally. That is, extend CA its own length and erect a perpendicular; or, if C is not a right angle, copy $\angle$ C. The dotted line in Fig. 5 at extreme right gives a hint that is probably unnecessary.

9. Approximately 59°2' or 59.04°. If the pupils do not know the tangent relation the teacher may wish to omit this exercise, though this informal allusion is an excellent way of introducing the pupil to the tangent of an angle and to a table of tangents. An occasional exercise of this sort that requires the pupil to consult reference material outside the textbook has the same general educative value in mathematics as in other subjects. The pupil must expect to get help occasionally from a dictionary, an encyclopedia, a table of square roots, a table of tangents, or the like, available in the school library or in certain class-rooms. The authors think it more important to reserve the appendix of a mathematics book for supplementary material that teacher and pupil cannot easily find elsewhere.

The authors are aware that numerical trigonometry grows immediately out of similar triangles in geometry. They do not wish, however, to interrupt the development of this logical presentation of geometry, commonly called demonstrative geometry, by a digression on trigonometry. They would much prefer that the pupil should have met the chief ideas of the numerical trigonometry of the right triangle in an earlier grade, these ideas being based on an even earlier treatment of similar triangles in intuitive geometry. There is growing recognition of the fact that all pupils in the seventh and eighth grades ought to meet the important ideas of geometry on an intuitional basis somewhere in these two grades. This is just as important for those who will never go on to demonstrative geometry as for those who will. It is recognized also that the numerical trigonometry of the right triangle is easier than demonstrative geometry, and easier than most of the algebra commonly taught in the ninth grade. For these and other reasons a little numerical trigonometry is now taught in many schools in the ninth grade, or even earlier. This bit of trigonometry is of particular importance for those pupils whose mathematical education will end with the ninth grade.

10. Triangles ABE and ACF are similar.

12. We could go on from here to develop the idea of area of a triangle, as outlined on page 222.

13. No.

14. No.

Page 74: Definition of altitude. Logically no reference to the altitudes of a triangle can be made until after Principle 11. That means that Exs. 10-12 on page 75 and Exs. 14-21 on pages 86 and 87 ought strictly to be deferred until after Principle 11. Any teacher who so wishes may do this, since no use has been made of these ideas thus prematurely introduced. It seems to the authors, however, that the "perpendicular" idea in these exercises is less important than more purely "triangle" ideas, and that these exercises fit in more naturally where they appear in the book than if grouped with exercises on the Pythagorean Theorem following Principles 11 and 12.

Note that the text states its intention of using the word "altitude" to mean not only the line, but the length of the line-segment. The same practice is adopted later with respect to "hypotenuse," "radius," and the like.

Page 75: Principle 7 is important on its own account, but would not have been allowed to intervene between Case 2 and Case 3 of the Principle of Similarity were it not needed to prove Case 3. The proof given of Principle 7 is unusual in that it applies Principle 5, which was worded so as to refer to two triangles, to a situation involving only a single isosceles triangle. It is clear from the text that an isosceles triangle can be considered to be similar to itself, regardless of the order in which the equal sides are read. Had we mentioned under Principle 5 that we intended to apply that Principle occasionally in this special manner, the remark would have conveyed no meaning. The authors deem it to be good teaching not to refer to this special application of Principle 5 until the need arises, as here in Principle 7.

Pages 77-78: Exercises.

4. Prove triangles ABC and ADC equal.

8. Yes.

Page 78: Principle 8. Note that the preceding exercises contain geometric configurations that resemble those needed in the proof of this theorem.

Page 80, lines 13 and 15. Read "sum of" both times, and "difference between" both times, to cover both cases shown in Fig. 15.

Pages 80-82: Exercises.

1. Angles ABC, ABF, EFG, EFB can vary. Also angles DCB, DCG, HGF, HGC.

4. Five distinct cross-braces can be made. Only two of these are needed for rigidity. These two can be chosen in ten different ways.

6. The fact that these ideas on equidistance are usually presented in a locus theorem receives recognition in Locus Theorem 4 in Chapter 9.

This has not prevented the authors, however, from exhibiting the essential ideas of this locus theorem in several exercises much earlier in the book in order that pupils may assimilate them gradually and make use of them as needed. The least useful of these ideas is the word "locus" itself, which in this book is withheld until the very end.

One good way to take the curse off the word "locus" and at the same time retain the very important locus concept in geometry is to do what the authors have done in BASIC GEOMETRY, namely, to introduce the ideas "a point equidistant from A and B - - -," "any point equidistant - - -," "every point equidistant - - -," and "all points equidistant - - -," and the converses of these, without mentioning "locus" at all. See the exercises on page 24; page 63, Ex. 16; page 81, Exs. 5-6; and page 88, Principle 10 (page 87 in the first printing of the book). Granting that the words "any," "every," "all" can give trouble in this connection, the authors believe that they have graded the steps so finely and have given such definite suggestions that pupils will easily prove the exercises and acquire incidentally the desired point of view. The basic difficulty with "any," "every," and "all" is that they imply generalization from particular instances, just as the variable x in algebra implies generalization from instances involving particular numbers. Generalization is a very important part of mathematics; it cannot be omitted. But if it gives difficulty, we can lead up to it gradually.

The authors regularly use the exercises as a medium for the introduction of ideas to be found in subsequent theorems. For although they think that learning from books is a gradual process, requiring repetition, they prefer to get the necessary repetition through organized - but apparently casual - previews than through the usual medium of organized - but dreary - reviews.

The chief difficulty in teaching demonstrative geometry is to hold the logical structure of the subject clearly in mind and at the same time allow reasonable play for the psychology of learning, which unfortunately is sufficiently formless to wreck the logical outlines of the subject if we are not careful. Nevertheless, the psychology cannot be denied. More effective than attack by solid phalanx is attack by infiltration, or "sifting through"; but the latter, despite its apparent informality, requires greater coördination of plan and operation than the former.

7. Each angle is 90°.

8. No.

Page 82: Principle 9. Note that Principle 8 is needed to prove Principles 9 and 10; that Principle 9 is needed to prove Principle 11; and that Principles 8, 6, and 9 are needed to prove the Pythagorean Theorem, Principle 12.

In the proof of Principle 9 the authors do not expect the pupil to give any reason for the statement " $\angle MBK = \angle ABC$"; none is needed. Nor do they expect the pupil to state that triangles MBK and ABC are similar before announcing that $MK = \frac{1}{2}AC$ and $\angle BMK = \angle A$; for the alternative statement of Case 1 of Similarity at the top of page 59 sanctions this shortening of the proof. Alternative statements of Case 2 and Case 3 of Similarity on pages 73 and 80 serve to sanction similar abbreviation elsewhere.

The teacher should understand that the rotating pencil on page 83 is merely an illustrative "aside" that may serve to stimulate the pupil's imagination. It is not an alternative proof. First of all, motion has no part in the postulates of this geometry. Second, even if it did have, this rotating about one point, moving to a second point and rotating some more, and so on, always keeping the pencil tangent to the surface

- 63 -

that contains the triangle, could be applied also to a spherical triangle and would seem to show that the sum of the angles of a spherical triangle is 180° also, which is not true. Actually the tilting of the pencil as we move from vertex to vertex of the spherical triangle reduces the plane angle that measures the dihedral at the preceding vertex, so that it is the sum of these reduced plane angles that is equal to 180°.

Page 84: Converse of Principle 9. In this instance it is more important to keep before the pupil the idea that a converse is not necessarily true than it is to exhibit the proof that this particular converse is true. If we do not raise the question at all, almost no one will think of it.

Pages 84-87: Exercises.

2. $\angle BCD = 180° - \angle ACB = \angle A + \angle B$

4-6. Divide into triangles by either one of the methods shown in Fig. 21 on page 59.

10. $\frac{n-2}{n} \cdot 180°$

11. 10

12. Except for the term "right triangle" this theorem could have been proved immediately after Case 2 of Similarity.

13. By Principle 9 and Case 2 of Similarity with $\underline{k}$ equal to 1.

Note: The authors use the term "mean proportional" instead of "geometric mean" because they prefer not to attach the adjective "geometric" to an idea that is essentially numerical. When in some later course in mathematics the pupil finds it necessary to distinguish arithmetic, geometric, and harmonic means he will recognize that all three are really numerical. That is, all three are arithmetic; and the so-called arithmetic mean, with its mid-point connotation, is quite as geometric as the so-called geometric mean.

14-15. Use Ex. 12 in this set of exercises. Although in their very

definition of the mean proportion relation the authors have shown
both ways of writing it, they purposely have given more emphasis to
the form $h^2 = mn$ in this text because any development of geometry
that makes use of numbers and algebra requires quick recognition of
the $h^2 = mn$ form of mean proportion. Euclid, having no algebra, made
free use of proportion to handle situations that we handle more read-
ily by means of equations. Many topics that he handled by mean
proportion we now handle by a simple quadratic equation. Indeed,
several of the thirteen books of Euclid's Elements are but geometric
developments of arithmetic and algebra for use in later books of the
Elements. Apollonius went much further in his study of conic sec-
tions than is covered by most college courses in analytic geometry,
but he was obliged to use proportion to disclose the relations that
we now obtain more easily by algebraic methods.

Some teachers may wonder why the authors do not use the results of
Ex. 15 to prove the Pythagorean Theorem at this point. In the note
on the definition of <u>altitude</u> on page 74 (page 60 of this manual)
it has already been pointed out, however, that Ex. 15 ought strictly
to be deferred until after Principle 11 has been proved; for Principle 11 is needed to establish the uniqueness of the altitude from a
given vertex of a triangle.

16. $h^2 = 5 \cdot 8$ and $h = 2\sqrt{10}$; $a^2 = 8 \cdot 13$ and $a = 2\sqrt{26}$; $b^2 = 5 \cdot 13$ and
$b = \sqrt{65}$

17. Some pupils will need not only the suggestion in the book to use
similar triangles, but will need the
further suggestion to use all three
pairs of similar triangles to be found
in the configuration.

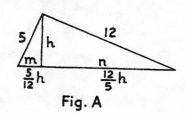

Fig. A

The similarity of the three right

- 65 -

triangles tells us first that $m = \frac{5}{12}$ h, n = $\frac{12}{5}$ h; and then either

that $\frac{h}{12} = \dfrac{5}{\left(\frac{5}{12} + \frac{12}{5}\right)h}$ or that $\frac{m}{5} = \dfrac{5}{m + \frac{144}{25}m}$. We have, therefore,

either h = $\frac{60}{13}$ or m = $\frac{25}{13}$. Finally, n = $\frac{144}{13}$.

It is not wise to suggest that the pupil get h first, because he can get m or n first equally well It would be proper to suggest, however, that three equations will be needed to determine the three unknowns and that these equations can be expected to come from three proportions This is a generalization in method that every pupil ought always to have as a ready resource.

18. h = $\sqrt{3} \cdot$ m; $\frac{a}{b} = \frac{m}{h} = \frac{1}{\sqrt{3}}$. See Fig. A.

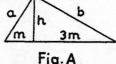

Fig. A

19. h = $\sqrt{k} \cdot$ m; $\frac{a}{b} = \frac{m}{h} = \frac{1}{\sqrt{k}}$.

20. $\frac{a}{b} = \sqrt{\frac{p}{q}}$

21. This is the same as Ex. 17 with numbers represented by letters. See Fig. B: m = $\frac{a}{b}$ h,

n = $\frac{b}{a}$ h; whence $\frac{m}{n} = \frac{a^2}{b^2}$. Also $\frac{h}{b} = \frac{a}{m + n} =$

$\dfrac{a}{\left(\frac{a}{b} + \frac{b}{a}\right)h}$; whence h = $\dfrac{ab}{\sqrt{a^2 + b^2}}$.

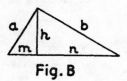

Fig. B

22. n(180°) - (n - 2)(180°) = 2(180°)

23. 82°. The reflex angle is just enough of a novelty to stimulate the pupil's imagination and add a bit of zest to an otherwise humdrum exercise. It does not make it appreciably harder. The pupil, by merely observing the 87° angle in one direction and the 74° angle in the opposite direction, can apply the resulting 13° appropriately.

The chief application of the exterior angle theorem is to this sort of surveying problem - technically known as a closed azimuth traverse - and the application is quite likely to include one or two reflex angles. The pupil does not need, and is not expected to need, a special theorem for polygons with reflex angles.

<u>Page 88</u>: Analysis for Principle 10. See note on Ex. 6, page 81

(page 61 of this manual). In the first and second printings of the book two methods of proof are suggested in the Analysis. The first method involves drawing a perpendicular from P to AB, but this is improper because the existence of any such perpendicular is not established until Principle 11 has been proved. In the third printing of the book the Analysis is changed to read as follows:

Analysis: We cannot prove that P lies on the perpendicular bisector of AB by drawing a line from P perpendicular to AB and showing that the midpoint of AB lies on this perpendicular, for we are not sure that this perpendicular exists until we have proved Principle 11. We may, however, connect P and the midpoint M of AB and show that PM is perpendicular to AB.

Page 89: Principle 11. Here, as in Principles 6, 7, and 8, the authors do not wish to do violence to the pupil's intuition by asking him to prove the obvious. In each such case, however, the authors have exhibited the proof in its proper sequence because they think that the pupil's imagination is more easily able to slight or ignore certain details of a whole than to reconstruct the whole from scattered pieces.

Page 90: Principle 12. The teacher should add that, although the idea contained in Principle 12 was known as early as 2600 B.C., it was not proved until about 550 B.C. That proof, by Pythagoras, was quite different from the proof given here in BASIC GEOMETRY.

The chief point of the analysis is to indicate that the "method of analysis" is sometimes unrewarding and that this is one such instance; the pupil can hardly be expected to discover the proof by his own unaided efforts.

The numerical case exhibited on page 91 is meant to be primarily an appeal to the eye. If the pupil will ponder and compare the successive enlargements of the original triangle, including the figure formed by placing two of these enlargements side by side, he will have the essence of the proof. It is to be hoped that he will appreciate the few and simple steps by which he has come from Case 1 of Similarity to a rigorous proof of one of the most important and famous theorems of all mathematics. This is properly the climax of this section of BASIC GEOMETRY.

The proof given on page 92 assumes that the pupil will easily grant that the figure A'B'D'C' is indeed a triangle, since angle A'C'D' is the sum of two right angles.

Page 93: Corollary 12a. The proof here is intended to be informal, condensing and telescoping the analysis and proof. Some teachers will think it a blemish that "$\angle C = 90°$" and "$\angle C' = 90°$" are not restated formally in the proof, but the authors think it is well not to waste the time of a class on formal details of this sort.

Corollary 12b is but a special case of Corollary 12a.

Page 94: Corollary 12c. There is nothing in the text that requires directed line-segments. In the obtuse case shown in Fig. 35, the sum of the undirected segments AD + DC is greater than AC; and the sum AB + BC, being greater even than AD + DC, is surely greater than AC. It is true that the relation AD + DC = AC of the acute case can be made to apply to this obtuse case by guarded use of directed distances, but this is quite unnecessary here.

The footnote on page 94 expresses the authors' unwillingness to ask pupils to supply reasons that depend on the fundamental concepts of the system of real numbers. This would be true in any other system of geometry and is not a peculiarity of BASIC GEOMETRY. In BASIC GEOMETRY, the system of real numbers is avowedly a cornerstone of the geometric structure; other geometric systems rely on number also, but do not explicitly avow it. The authors can think of no adequate explanation that they could reasonably demand of pupils in support of the statement "AB = AB";

and they shrink from the task of building up the logical steps that would establish the statement "If unequal numbers are added to unequal numbers in the same order, the sums are unequal in the same order."

It is better to take the system of real numbers for granted and not bother the pupils with explanations that seem not to explain. For the convenience of teachers, however, the first steps in establishing the system of real numbers are given at the end of BASIC GEOMETRY in a separate section entitled "Laws of Number." The authors recognize that teachers who have never seen these "laws" set down explicitly will be momentarily stunned by the forbidding appearance of certain of them. These matters are an important part of the professional kit of teachers of algebra and geometry, however, and cannot be entirely ignored; furthermore, interest in them among teachers is growing fast. Contrast, for example, the exposition of negative number in algebras of twenty years ago and in algebras today. The authors hope that by calling attention to certain gaps in the logical development they can lead the pupils to a better appreciation of the nature of a logical system than could be got by glossing over the difficulties that beset every logical system.

It is important to note that Corollary 12c asserts, in effect, that the straight line distance between two points is less than any broken line distance between these points. It is even more important to note that it does not assert that the shortest distance between two points is the length of the straight line-segment between the two points. BASIC GEOMETRY makes no pronouncement as to that.

Page 95: Corollary 12d. The "shortest distance" means the shortest straight line distance.

Pages 95-98: Exercises. The limitation of answers to significant figures is not intended to impose a heavy burden on either teacher or pupil. The authors recognize that a consistent and precise use of

- 69 -

significant figures requires a high degree of judgment as well as of knowledge. Nevertheless, the general spirit of significant figures can be easily acquired even by pupils in the seventh grade, and flagrant violations of this spirit are obvious. It is these flagrant violations that we wish most of all to avoid. All we need is a few simple rules which, though not absolutely reliable in all cases, serve well enough for our purposes. The chief interest of the authors is that the pupils shall recognize that they themselves can determine the answer to their inquiry "How far shall we carry this out?" and shall see that the answer depends, not on convenience or on teacher's whim, but on the accuracy of the data.

If the length of a rectangle is measured to the nearest foot, the recorded length may be in error - that is, may differ from the true length - by not more than half a foot. Similarly for the width. If length and width are recorded as 34 and 21 feet respectively, the true area must lie between the product 33.5 times 20.5 and the product 34.5 times 21.5; that is, the true area must lie between 686.75 square feet and 741.75 square feet. Thus there is a range of 55 square feet within which the true area lies. The product of 34 times 21 is 714, which is almost midway in this range. We cannot submit the product 714 square feet as the true area without recording the possibility of an error up to 27.5 square feet either side of 714. That is, the second digit in 714 may be in error by almost 3. Consequently the third digit, 4, is quite meaningless and we ought to replace it by 0. If we keep the 4 in the answer we are guilty of misrepresenting the accuracy of our result.

From this numerical case it looks as though the product of a two-digit number times a two-digit number (each derived from measurement) is itself liable to serious error in the second digit. Indeed, in the example just shown, the first digit of the product is in doubt also; but that is due to our method of writing numbers rather than to matters

- 70 -

pertaining to accuracy. We ought to record the area as 710 square feet, recognizing the possibility of an _error_ of almost 3 in the second digit and occasional need of _altering_ the first digit by 1 downwards. Further considerations of a similar sort lead us to keep not more than n digits in the product of two n-digit numbers; n digits in the quotient of two n-digit numbers; and n digits in the square root of an n-digit number.

Significant figures are figures that give information that is at least fairly reliable. Figures that are only a pretense and are really meaningless must be replaced by zeros. Zeros of this sort must be distinguished in some way from zeros that are truly significant. The position of the decimal point has nothing to do with significant figures.

The teacher may find it helpful to regard the product of two measures from the point of view of per cent error. Thus the measure l may represent a true length of $l(1 \pm \epsilon)$, where ϵ represents the per cent error in l. Similarly η may represent the per cent error in w, so that the true product of l times w is not lw, but $lw(1 \pm \epsilon \pm \eta \pm \epsilon \eta)$. From this it appears that the per cent error in the product lw is not greater than $\epsilon + \eta$, the sum of the per cent errors in l and w.* Either by this method of per cent errors, or by contemplating the product of the two smallest n-digit numbers and the product of the two largest n-digit numbers, we see that we are justified in keeping not more than n digits in the product of two n-digit numbers. The teacher can test this in the case of two-digit numbers by considering the products $(10 \pm \frac{1}{2}) \cdot (10 \pm \frac{1}{2})$, $(30 \pm \frac{1}{2}) \cdot (30 \pm \frac{1}{2})$, $(33 \pm \frac{1}{2}) \cdot (33 \pm \frac{1}{2})$, and $(99 \pm \frac{1}{2}) \cdot (99 \pm \frac{1}{2})$, both as here written and by the method of per cent errors.

For a more extensive discussion of significant figures see Aaron Bakst, "Approximate Computation," Bureau of Publications, Teachers College, Columbia, 1937.

---

*We purposely ignore the trivial term $\epsilon \eta$.

1. (d) Expected answer is $\sqrt{2}$, or 1.4. If a pupil, having significant figures in mind, submits the answer 2, he is wrong; for $\sqrt{2}$ is not included in the range $2 \pm \frac{1}{2}$.

   (m) $p^2 + q^2$ (n) 16.6, or 17

   (o) 11.3, or 11   (p) 486

2. (b) $\sqrt{3}$, or 1.7   (e) $s\sqrt{3}$ (i) 12.4, or 12

   (j) 8.7   (k) 171

3. 20.2, or 20, miles

4. First prove in two ways that one side of a $30° - 60°$ triangle, namely the side opposite the $30°$ angle, is equal in length to half the hypotenuse. Then show by the Pythagorean Theorem that this is the shortest side of the triangle, as in Ex. 2(g) above.

5. The left hand diagram in Fig. 38 suggests one method. A second method is to draw from the mid-point M of HK the line MN perpendicular to KL. Prove $KN = \frac{1}{2}KL$; then $NL = KN$; and $ML = MK = KL$; whence $\angle K = 60°$.

Fig. A

8. $90°$, by converse of Pythagorean Theorem

11. 5 inches, 12.4 inches, 12.6 inches

12. 13 inches

13. Use converse of Pythagorean Theorem, noting that
$$(p^2 - q^2)^2 + (2pq)^2 = (p^2 + q^2)^2.$$

14. $p = 2$, $q = 1$

15. $p = 3$, $q = 2$

18. By Corollary 12d, the shortest distance from A to BD is AD. Therefore $AB > AD$. Similarly, $CB > CD$. Therefore $AB + BC > AC$.

19. In Fig. 25, $b^2 = cm$

$$\frac{a^2 = cn}{b^2 + a^2 = c(m + n) = c^2}$$

20. From Corollary 12c, $AB + BC > AC$. Therefore $AB > AC - BC$.

21. $\angle$ DEP + $\angle$ DPE = $\angle$ DFP + $\angle$ DPF. $\angle$ DPE $<$ $\angle$ DPF. Therefore

$\angle$ DEP $>$ $\angle$ DFP.

22. From similar triangles, $\frac{1}{x} = \frac{x}{2}$

23. x^2, area of inner square, equals $\frac{1}{2}$ of 2^2, area of outer square.

Pages 100-103: Exercises.

1. $\frac{33}{19}$ x 4 inches

2. $\frac{7}{5}$ x 22 cm.

3. $\frac{5}{4}$t + $\frac{5}{4}$t + t = 21

Sides are 6, $7\frac{1}{2}$, $7\frac{1}{2}$.

4. Take $\angle$ AOB = 30°, OB = $\frac{3}{16}$ in.;

$\angle$ AOC = 60°, OC = $\frac{3}{8}$ in.;

and so forth.

6. 36°

8. Use result of Ex. 10 on page 85. Actually the formula $\frac{n-4}{n}$ (180°) applies only to stars formed by joining each side of the regular polygon to the side that is next but one to it, keeping the same order throughout. To consider the stars formed by joining each side to the side that is next but two, next but three, and so forth, it is better to circumscribe a circle about the polygon and use the angle between two secants; but this is not available until the pupil has arrived at Ex. 6 on page 148. In the case of the regular 9-gon, the several possible stars have angles of 100°, 60°, or 20°. The stars that can be formed from a regular 12-gon have angles of 120°, 90°, 60°, 30°, or 0°.

9. By Case 2 of Similarity

10. Prove by Ex. 9.

11. Given right triangle ABC with right angle at C; M, the mid-point of BC; N, the mid-point of AC; and I, the intersection of the perpendicular bisectors of the two shorter sides, assumed to be not on the hypotenuse AB.

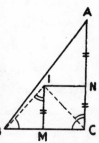

Fig. A

IB = IC. $\angle$ IBM = $\angle$ ICM. $\angle$ BIM = 90° - $\angle$ IBM = 90° - $\angle$ ICM = $\angle$ ICN.

- 73 -

Therefore right triangles IBM and ICN are equal, and IM = NC = ½ AC.

Therefore right triangles IBM and ABC are similar, ∠ IBM = ∠ ABC,
I lies on AB, and BI = ½ BA.

Alternate proof: From Ex. 9 of this set of exercises we know that
M, the mid-point of the hypotenuse, must lie on each perpendicular
bisector and so must be the point of intersection of both perpendicular bisectors.

12. The diagonals of each face are s√2; the diagonals of the cube are
s√3.

13. In three dimensional exercises informal proofs are not only permis-
sible but expected. In this case all that is expected is that the
pupil recognize that in a cube of side s the diagonals of a face are
perpendicular whereas two diagonals of the cube, like AG and CE, are
diagonals also of a rectangle with unequal sides and hence are not
perpendicular. Inasmuch as the terms rectangle and square have not
yet been officially defined in this geometry, these figures and their
common properties are meant to be taken for granted by the pupil. It
is not expected that he supply the following details.

In the square ABCD the isosceles right triangles ABC and BAD are
equal; angles CAB and DBA are equal to 45°; therefore AC and BD intersect at right angles.

In the rectangle ACGE the non-isosceles right triangles ACG and CAE
are equal; angles GAC and ECA are equal, but not equal to 45°; therefore AG and CE intersect at some angle other than 90°.

14. Any two of the four diagonals of the cube are related as are AG and
CE in the preceding exercise.

15. In other words, find the angle between the diagonals of the rectangle ACGE, in which AC = s√2, CG = s, and each diagonal = s√3.

- 74 -

Tan $\angle$ GAC $= \dfrac{1}{\sqrt{2}}$. Therefore $\angle$ GAC $= 35.3°$ ($35° \; 18'$) and the desired

angle is approximately $70.5°$.

17. Height of house $= 18 + 6\sqrt{5}$

$(AB)^2 = (18 + 6\sqrt{5})^2 + 1744$

$\qquad = 2248 + 216(2.236)$

$\qquad = 2248 + 483$

$AB = 52.3$

18. $48.2° = 48°11'$

19. $2\sqrt{7} = 5.3$ inches

20. 3.2 inches

21. $500 \times \dfrac{5}{6} = 416\dfrac{2}{3}$

Lesson Plan Outline: 12 lessons

1. Cor. 13a, b; Theorem 14, Cor. 14a

2. Theorems 15 and 16

3-7. Exercises, pages 113-117

8-9. Theorem 17 through page 125

10-12. Exercises, pages 126-130, mixing in the three-
dimensional exercises with the others

Page 106: Existence versus definition. In Theorem 13 we first establish the existence of parallel lines and then, on page 108, we define parallel lines. From a strictly logical point of view it is possible first to define, and then to establish the existence of that which has been defined. But because this order seems unnatural to most people we say "In general we prefer not to define anything until we have first shown that it exists."

The statement of Theorem 13 does not contain the qualification that the second line is in the same plane as the given line. It would make the statement too cumbersome to include this, and it is not necessary; for it has already been made clear that this is a plane geometry that we are developing. Were we not confined to the plane determined by the given line and the given point, the second sentence of the proof (lines 14-15 on page 107) would be untrue. Certain pupils may be interested to ferret this out. In the definition of parallel lines on page 108 the qualification "in the same plane" is inserted because it is easy to do so and avoids confusion when the pupil goes on to solid geometry. The teacher may wish to tell the class that lines that are not in the same plane and do not meet are called skew lines.

In the proof of Theorem 13 on page 107, lines 14 and 15, we need both

- 76 -

Principle 3 and Principle 4 to establish the unique perpendicular to a given line at a point of the line. The word "perpendicular" is defined on page 50 in terms of 90 degrees, which involves the straight angle and Principle 4. The uniqueness of this perpendicular depends on Principle 3, as set forth on page 54 of BASIC GEOMETRY.

On page 108 and thereafter we use the word "parallel" both as adjective and as noun. Concerning the use of the word "all" in the definition of a "system of parallels" at the bottom of page 108, see the note on "all" as used on page 118, line 13, farther on in this chapter of the manual.

Page 109: Transversal is defined as a line that cuts "a number of other lines." This number of other lines may be only one, or two, or more than two.

Both teacher and pupil should note that Theorems 14-16 and the exercises on pages 113-117 are concerned with parallels that are cut by a general transversal. The next section of this chapter, beginning with Theorem 17, is concerned with parallels that are cut by a perpendicular transversal.

Page 109: Theorem 14. Note that this theorem is so worded as to embrace all three cases that other geometry texts see fit to distinguish in this geometric situation. In BASIC GEOMETRY, however, we see no need of playing up the idea that "vertical angles are equal." We merely call attention to this in Exs. 10, 12, and 13 on page 52 as an obvious result of numbering half-lines with common end-point so that number differences measure angles. Consequently this geometry does not need to distinguish, or even mention, "alternate-interior" angles, "corresponding" angles, "exterior-interior" angles, or "interior angles on the same side of the transversal." Actually the last of these four phrases is referred to in

- 77 -

the note at the bottom of page 109 in order to satisfy teachers who wish to check off the familiar ideas of geometry as they studied it, and to identify the occurrence of these same ideas in BASIC GEOMETRY.

Similarly the terms "supplementary angles" and "complementary angles" are mentioned on page 111 to satisfy teachers who think these terms are valuable. The authors of BASIC GEOMETRY prefer not to emphasize them.

Pages 113-117: Exercises.

1. Merely insures that the pupil supply the details of the proof referred to on page 111, lines 1-2.

4. AB = CD, from Ex. 2

6. Prove BC = DA and apply Ex. 5.

7. Since the sum of all four angles of the quadrilateral is 360°, by Ex. 3 on page 84, the sum of two adjacent angles is 180°. See note, bottom of page 109.

9. Use Principle 10.

12. JK = 1.8; KL = 2.7

15. It is not necessary that the points of intersection in Fig. 8 be lettered in order to facilitate class discussion. The desired answer is merely "All the acute angles are equal and all the obtuse angles are equal. All the shortest distances are equal, and - if both double tracks are equally spaced - all corresponding longer distances are equal."

16. Since AB = H'J', rs = 1, and r and s are reciprocals.

17. Merely replace AH and BJ in Fig. 4, page 111, by AJ and BH.

18. Use Case 2 of Similarity.

19. By drawing A'A and extending through A, show that $\angle A' = \angle A$. Similarly for B'B and C'C. Therefore the triangles are similar, and $B'C' = \frac{8}{5} \cdot 4$ and $C'A' = \frac{8}{5} \cdot 6$.

20. First method: Use Theorem 15.

Second method: Draw a second parallel through B and apply Theorem 16.

21. Use Case 1 of Similarity and Theorem 14.

23. Either prove the upper and lower triangles similar, or draw a parallel through the intersection of the diagonals and apply Theorem 16.

25. By means of equal angles prove that triangle ABR is isosceles. Use Ex. 20, page 115.

26. By means of equal angles prove that triangle ABQ is isosceles.

28. Draw a diagonal of the quadrilateral and prove that two of the lines in question are parallel to this diagonal and that each of these two lines is equal to half the diagonal. Either diagonal will serve, whether the four vertices are in the same plane or not. In the latter case the quadrilateral is called a "skew quadrilateral."

29. The pupil will take the random line in the same plane as the parallelogram. Use Ex. 24 on page 116. The length of the perpendicular drawn to the random line from the point of intersection of the diagonals is equal to one fourth of the sum of the perpendiculars from the vertices.

Question for discussion: What happens if the random line passes through one vertex of the parallelogram and has no other point in common with it? What happens if the random line intersects two adjacent sides of the parallelogram? If the random line passes through the point of intersection of the diagonals?

Page 118: Corollary 17a is a corollary of the definition of rectangle immediately preceding this corollary. Prove the corollary by means of Exs. 2 and 7 on page 113.

The term "rectangle" is _defined_ on page 118, line 5, as a quadrilateral each angle of which is a right angle. This definition and Corollary 17a permit the further <u>description</u> of a rectangle (page 118, line 9) as an equiangular parallelogram. The statements following this description serve to <u>define</u> the terms "rhombus" and "square."

Page 118, line 13: "We have seen - - -." This refers back to page 110, line 8, and thence to page 108. When we say "all the lines perpendicular to a given line" (page 118, lines 13 and 14) we have in mind a system of perpendiculars - and hence also a system of parallels - that is as numerous as the points on a line. This means that the number of lines in the system of parallels referred to on page 118, and also on page 108, is the non-denumerable infinity of the continuum. The number of lines in "the collection of lines - - - - called a <u>rectangular network</u>" on page 118 is also equal to this non-denumerable infinity of the continuum; for the lines in a rectangular network can be paired with the lines in a system of parallels. (See E. V. Huntington, <u>The Continuum and Other Types of Serial Order</u>, Harvard University Press, 1917, 1938.)

Page 119: Coördinates. We purposely use "x-coördinate" and "y-coördinate" instead of "abscissa" and "ordinate," because the two former are clear, unmistakable, and in general use among mathematicians.

Page 121: Exercises.

1. The suggestion "- or any other convenient distance as the unit -" is meant to imply that printed squared paper is not necessary for these few exercises and that the pupil can draw his own network in each case.

2. Slopes are $\frac{5}{3}$; $\frac{2}{4}$; $\frac{3}{2}$; $\frac{11}{26}$.

4. OA = $\sqrt{34}$

   OB = $2\sqrt{5}$

   OC = $\sqrt{13}$

   OD = $\frac{\sqrt{797}}{4}$

   OE = OF = OG = $\sqrt{34}$

   OH = $2\sqrt{5}$

   OI = $\sqrt{29}$

   OJ = $\frac{\sqrt{65}}{2}$ or $\sqrt{16.25}$

   OK = $\frac{\sqrt{74}}{2}$ or $\sqrt{18.5}$

- 80 -

5. AC = $\sqrt{5}$

   BD = $\dfrac{\sqrt{109}}{4}$

   AG = $8\sqrt{2}$

   KF = $\sqrt{136}$

   KK = $\dfrac{\sqrt{130}}{2}$

   CJ = $\dfrac{\sqrt{233}}{2}$

   JK = $\dfrac{\sqrt{13}}{2}$

   ID = $\dfrac{\sqrt{1285}}{4}$ = 8.96

   KD = $\dfrac{\sqrt{2041}}{4}$ = 11.3

   JD = $\dfrac{\sqrt{1781}}{4}$ = 10.5$^+$

6. Slope is $-\frac{1}{2}$.

7. Slopes are 2; -1; $-\frac{5}{9}$.

8. Slope of GK is $\frac{1}{3}$; slope of BD is $\frac{3}{10}$. The slope of HB is 0.

9. IA has steepest slope, 10. GK, though inclined more steeply to the x-axis than IA, has no slope.

Page 122: Theorem 18. Complete the proof by showing that $\angle$ LPQ = $\angle$ MPR.

Page 123: The equation of a line. The authors wish to show at this point how the usual ideas concerning the straight line in analytic geometry can be developed from the fundamental concepts of BASIC GEOMETRY. Similarly, on pages 133-135, they begin the analytic treatment of the circle. But having made this connection with analytic geometry, they do not wish to go farther; for an accurate and reasonably complete treatment of straight line and circle by the methods of analytic geometry would make too long an interruption in the main theme of this book and would introduce too many difficulties. The step from the graph of 2x - 3y - 5 = 0 in elementary algebra to the general equation of the first degree in analytic geometry, namely ax + by + c = 0, is much harder than most secondary-school teachers believe it to be.

In considering (near the bottom of page 123) the equation of the line through (a, b) that is parallel to the x-axis, the treatment in the text ought strictly to follow the pattern for the general straight line as

- 81 -

set forth in lines 9-12 higher up on this page. That is, it ought to
show not only that the y-coordinate of every point on this line is b,
but also that every point whose y-coordinate is b lies on this line; and
similarly for the equation of the line through (a, b) that is perpendicular to the x-axis. Since, however, these two special cases usually give
pupils more trouble than the ordinary oblique cases, it seems wiser not
to insist on a complication in the development that the pupil would probably not appreciate.

Page 124: Exercises.

1. $\dfrac{y}{x} = \dfrac{4}{5}$

2. $\dfrac{y}{x} = -\dfrac{3}{2}$

3. ay = bx, or bx - ay = 0.

Page 125. A brick has three planes of symmetry. A cube has nine
planes of symmetry. A man has one plane of symmetry.

Two symmetric plane triangles will coincide if one is rotated through
$180°$ about the axis of symmetry; two symmetric spherical triangles cannot
be made to coincide by this sort of rotation.

The third paragraph on page 125 of BASIC GEOMETRY will be revised
to read:

"Fig. 25 has no axis of symmetry. If, however, we rotate this figure
in the plane of the paper about the point O through an angle of $180°$, it
coincides with its original position. Whenever a $180°$-rotation of this
sort about a point O causes a figure to coincide with its original position, the figure is said to be symmetric with respect to the point O and
O is called the center of symmetry of the figure."

Every square, every rectangle, every regular hexagon, has a center of
symmetry. No triangle, not even an equilateral triangle, and no pentagon
has a center of symmetry.

Almost every leaf in nature is symmetric with respect to an axis, if

- 82 -

we ignore minor discrepancies. But mulberry, sassafras, poison ivy, and poison oak have asymmetric leaves, often symmetrically grouped. This distinctive characteristic is particularly important in the case of the poisonous ones.

A geometric figure is symmetric with respect to a point O if every point P of the figure (except O) has a corresponding point P' in the figure such that PP' is bisected by O.

Pages 126-130: Exercises.

1. The seven figures have 2, 5, 6, 4, I, 2, 0 axes of symmetry respectively. All but the second and fifth have symmetry with respect to a point. The fourth, fifth, sixth show close relation to a network.

2. The left leaf, or leaflet, usually exhibits left-handed asymmetry; the middle leaf, or leaflet, is symmetric; and the right leaf, or leaflet, usually shows right-handed asymmetry.

3. Use Theorem 15 and Principle 6.

   Incidentally, the teacher should lead the pupils to observe that the three pairs of similar triangles in Fig. 28 all have the same factor of proportionality, but that no triangle of one pair is similar to a triangle of another pair.

4. $\frac{PB}{PB'} = \frac{AB}{A'B'} = \frac{BC}{B'C'} = \frac{QB}{QB'}$
   Therefore $\frac{PB'}{PB} - 1 = \frac{QB'}{QB} - 1$, and $\frac{BB'}{PB} = \frac{BB'}{QB}$.
   Since PB = QB, P and Q coincide and the three lines are concurrent.
   If AB = A'B' and BC = B'C', the three lines are parallel.

5. Use Theorem 15 and Principle 6.

6. Using Fig. 30, assume that AA' and CC' meet at P and that AA' and BB' meet at Q.
   $\frac{PA}{PA'} = \frac{AC}{A'C'} = \frac{AB}{A'B'}$
   $\frac{QA}{QA'} = \frac{AB}{A'B'}$
   Therefore $\frac{PA}{PA'} = \frac{QA}{QA'}$; $\frac{PA}{PA'} - 1 = \frac{QA}{QA'} - 1$; and $\frac{AA'}{PA'} = \frac{AA'}{QA'}$.

So P and Q coincide and the three lines are concurrent.

7. If the triangles are equal, AA', and BB', and CC' are parallel.

8. Using Fig. 31, follow the proof of Ex. 6 except that A' is now replaced by A" and that we now write $\frac{PA}{PA''} + 1 = \frac{QA}{QA''} + 1$.

9. As indicated in Fig. 32, draw two random lines through P to meet $\underline{l}$
and $\underline{m}$. Complete the triangle as shown and draw another triangle
similar to the first so that the two triangles have their sides respectively parallel. The line joining P and the corresponding vertex
in the second triangle is the desired line. (Or else replace this
explanation by the following: "Use Ex. 6 above, as indicated in
Fig. 32.")

10. $\frac{15}{4}$ miles an hour

11. The perpendicular bisectors of opposite sides of a rectangle coincide. The perpendicular bisectors of adjacent sides meet in a point
that is equidistant from all four vertices of the rectangle. Since
the diagonals of a rectangle are equal (Principle 5) and bisect each
other (page 113, Ex. 4), their intersection also is equidistant from
all four vertices of the rectangle and hence must lie on the perpendicular bisector of each side of the rectangle.

12. If all three planes are perpendicular to a fourth plane and no two
of the three planes are parallel, they intersect two at a time in
three parallel lines. If two of these three planes are parallel,
the three planes intersect in two parallel lines. If all three of
these planes are parallel, they have no point in common.

The answers to Exs. 13-21 given below are much more detailed than
can be fairly expected of pupils. The point of these exercises is to get
the pupil to consider and discuss certain three-dimensional analogues of
the ideas set forth in the earlier part of this chapter. It is desired
that the pupil shall think in three dimensions sufficiently to see the

relations involved in these exercises. It is not expected that he supply proofs.

13. Call the two given parallel lines l and m. If the "other" line, m, and the plane containing l have a point in common, this point will lie not only in this plane but in the plane determined by l and m. That is, it will lie on the intersection of these two planes, namely l. But this would mean that a point of m lies also on l, which is impossible. So m and the plane containing l can have no point in common.

14. If the two planes have a point in common they also have a line in common. If any point of this line be joined to the ends of that segment of the given perpendicular line that is included between the two planes, the resulting triangle will contain two angles of 90°, which is impossible.

15. If the two lines of intersection have a point in common, this point must be common to the two parallel planes, which is impossible.

16. Given lines l and m in Fig. 33, join the point of intersection of l and the first plane with the point of intersection of m and the third plane, forming an auxiliary line shown in the figure. Apply Theorem 16 to l and the auxiliary line, and again to the auxiliary line and m.

17. Use Ex. 15 on this page, Theorem 15, Principle 6, and Ex. 5 on page 127.

18. If "the plane of these lines" is not parallel to the given plane it has a line in common with the given plane. This line of intersection cannot be parallel to both the given intersecting lines; it must have a point in common with one of them. This point, therefore, must be common to the given plane and to a line that is parallel to the given plane. This is impossible.

19. One of the given lines and the parallel through any point of it to

the other given line determine a plane that is parallel to "the other given line," by Ex. 13 on page 129. Since there is only one such parallel through any point of the first given line, there is only one such parallel plane through this "any point." Further, this plane contains the parallel through each of the other points of the first given line.

20. Through the given point there are two lines one of which is parallel to one of the given skew lines, while the other is parallel to the other of the given skew lines. These two "parallels" determine a plane, and the only plane, that is parallel to both the given skew lines. If the given point lies on one of the given skew lines we have the situation of Ex. 19 on this page.

21. If there is a common perpendicular to two given skew lines, it will be perpendicular also to a random plane that is parallel to the two skew lines. So, of all the perpendiculars to a given skew line we need consider only those that are perpendicular also to this random plane. These perpendiculars lie in the plane that contains the given skew line and is perpendicular to the random plane. Similarly, we need consider only those perpendiculars to the other skew line that lie in the plane that contains this other skew line and is perpendicular to the random plane. The line of intersection of these two planes each of which is perpendicular to the "random parallel plane" is the common perpendicular to the two skew lines.

Page 133: Circle. In order not to clutter up the definition of "circle" in lines 7-8 with a forbidding array of words, the authors have used the phrase "all the points" to stand for "all the points and no other points." The "other points" are taken care of in a subsequent sentence, lines 13-16, that considers all points whose distance from O is either less than or greater than r. In the equation discussed in lines 21-23, r varies from circle to circle but is constant for any particular circle. This "variable constant" r is called a parameter and must not be confused with the true variables, x and y, of the equation.

On page 134 the first paragraph associates the points on a circle with half-lines having a common end-point O in order to lead up to the definition of "arc" in the following paragraph. This association serves also to establish the fact - not mentioned in the text - that the circle is a continuous curve; for in Principle 3 the linking of the system of real numbers with all the half-lines having a common end-point establishes the continuity of these half-lines in the same way that in

Principle 1 the linking of the system of real numbers with all the points on an endless line establishes the continuity of the endless line. These ideas concerning continuity are withheld in this book until Chapter 8, pages 228-231.

Page 134: Minor arc. In the discussion of "angle" as a geometric configuration on page 46 the idea of "lesser angle" was admittedly used prematurely. This idea was legalized later by the discussion of angle measure under Principle 3. Unfortunately we cannot jump with equal rapidity from the definition of arc to the definition of arc length. So, although we may distinguish arcs, defined as aggregates of points on a circle corresponding to certain half-lines, by means of their central angles, we have no right to allow "lesser central angle" to impute the idea "lesser length" to the corresponding arc. We must restrict the implication of the term lesser, or minor, arc to this association with lesser central angle and must leave out all idea of length until we come to Chapter 7. We do the same with respect to equal arcs on page 135. Of course, everyone knows intuitively what the final decision about arc lengths is to be. But officially we need first to make clear what is meant by the length of a circle, and this requires the usual polygon and limit technique.

Although it would be possible at this time to consider directed arcs in terms of directed central angles, the use of signs in this connection would have to be construed as applying only to the central angles involved and as carrying no implication concerning the lengths of the directed arcs. This is so unnatural that the matter of directed arcs is deferred until page 209, where it is possible then to allow the sign of a directed arc to carry also an implication as to magnitude. See bracketed answer to question 5, page 135.

- 88 -

1. (a) $x^2 + y^2 = 4$ (c) $x^2 + y^2 = 9.61$

   (b) $x^2 + y^2 = 25$ (d) $x^2 + y^2 = \frac{4}{9}$

2. (a) 3   (c) 1.9   (e) $\sqrt{2}$

   (b) $2\sqrt{2}$ (d) $\frac{3}{2}$

3. One, the point (0, 0)

4. None

5. Arc BC = arc DE = 25   Arc BC = arc CE = 65

   Arc BE = arc FA = 90   Arc BF = arc EA = 235

   [Arc ED = arc CB = -335]

6. On the half-line numbered 80, or 260.

Page 136: Diameter. See the discussion of "circle" and "diameter" on pages 14-15 of BASIC GEOMETRY.

Page 136, third paragraph. Here we have an example of a variable approaching a limit and equaling its limit; and an example also of a variable approaching a limit but never equaling its limit. The teacher will do well to emphasize this matter - though chiefly as an aside - because the word limit usually occurs in elementary geometry in cases where the variable does not equal its limit. This leads the pupil to infer, erroneously, that a variable can never equal its limit, and it is wise to try to prevent his getting this false impression.

Page 137: Exercises.

1. We expect "equally spaced" to be understood as "having equal central angles." The idea of equal arcs is not yet available.

2. Apply Case 3 of Similarity, pages 78-80, to the two triangles.

3. Use Corollary 12b, page 93.

5. Use the Pythagorean Theorem and Ex. 3, page 137.

6. Use the Pythagorean Theorem. The pupil is expected to recognize

intuitively that r^2 - (shorter)^2 is greater than r^2 - (greater)^2.
He is not expected to quote the eighth law on page 288 in support
of his argument. See page 234.

7. Each chord corresponds to a central angle of $60°$.

Pages 140-145: Exercises.

1. Use indirect method - suppose that perpendicular does not pass through
the center; then Theorem 21, and unique perpendicular idea on page 54.

2. Use indirect method - suppose that the perpendicular does not pass
through the point of tangency; then Theorem 21 and Principle 11,
page 88.

3-4. Use Corollary 15a, page 111, and Corollary 12b, page 93.

5. Use Theorem 21, Corollary 15a, and Ex. 2 on page 141 to prove that the
diameter through one point of tangency passes through the other point
of tangency also.

6-7. Use Ex. 3 and Theorem 19.

8. Use Corollary 12b.

9. Use Ex. 8.

10. The sum of one pair of opposite central angles is equal to the sum
of the other pair. Draw radii to the four points of tangency; use
Ex. 8 and Corollary 12b.

11. As in Ex. 9.

12. As in Ex. 11, the sum of alternate sides of a circumscribed n-gon is
equal to the sum of the remaining sides when n is even, but not when
n is odd.

13. The authors use the word "show" instead of "prove" in this exercise
to indicate that the pupil is expected to exhibit satisfactory diagrams only, but no proofs. The following statements are for the
teacher only. Whenever the expression r - r' occurs in these statements it is assumed that r is greater than r'.

- 90 -

If the circles should have a point in common when OO' is greater than $r + r'$, then - by Corollary 12c - $r + r'$ would be greater than OO': an obvious contradiction.

If the circles should have a point in common when OO' is less than $r - r'$, then - by Ex. 20 on page 98 - $r - r'$ would be less than OO': another contradiction.

If, when $OO' = r + r'$, the circles should have a point in common but not on OO', then - by Corollary 12c - $r + r'$ would also be greater than OO': impossible.

If, when $OO' = r - r'$, the circles should have a point in common but not on OO' extended, then - by Ex. 20 on page 98 - $r - r'$ would also be less than OO': impossible.

In these last two cases the circles can clearly have one point in common, and this common point must lie on OO' or on OO' extended. That the circles might have a second point in common, not on OO' or on OO' extended, has just been shown to be impossible.

Finally, when $r - r' < OO' < r + r'$, if the circles should have a point in common on OO' or on OO' extended, then OO' is either simultaneously less than $r + r'$ and equal to $r + r'$, or else simultaneously greater than $r - r'$ and equal to $r - r'$: both impossible.

14. By Principle 10, page 87, and Principle 2, page 44.

15. If the two circles should have three distinct points A, B, C in common, then OO' would be the perpendicular bisector of AB and of AC at the same time; and this is impossible, as there cannot be two lines from A perpendicular to OO'.

Exs. 13 and 15 establish the existence of two and not more than two points common to two circles. It is proper then on page 143 to define the terms "points of intersection" and "common chord."

16. Use Ex. 1.

17. The teacher can vary this by asking for a single diagram showing several interesting steps in the transit of a small circle (moon) across a larger circle (sun).* He can ask also whether an eclipse of the sun by the moon appears to an observer on the earth to be an example of a small circle passing across a larger circle.

18. 3.99 inches

19. 0.87 inches

20. 4.8 + 4.4 + 4.0 = 13.2 inches

21. (a) $00' > r + r'$ (c) $r - r' < 00' < r + r'$ (e) $00' < r - r'$

    (b) $00' = r + r'$ (d) $00' = r - r'$

22. $00'$. If $r = r'$, a second axis of symmetry is the perpendicular bisector of $00'$ in cases (a), (b), and (c).

23. From a point P on the common tangent a tangent to either circle is equal to PT, by Ex. 8 on page 141.

24. This is a special case of the preceding exercise.

25-26. If the common external tangents meet at T, then the angle between these tangents is bisected by TO (Ex. 8 on page 141). This same angle is bisected also by TO'. Therefore TO and TO' are (parts of) the same line, and T lies on $00'$.

If the two circles in Ex. 25 have equal radii, their common external tangents do not meet.

Pages 145-146: Theorem 22 and Corollaries 22a, 22b, 22c. We have defined "arc" (page 134) in intimate connection with "central angle" and have then employed the phrase "a central angle has an arc." On page 135 we have defined equal arcs as having equal radii and equal central angles, but have disavowed any intention of implying at this time that equal arcs, thus defined, have equal lengths. When in Corollary 22a we say that equal inscribed angles have equal arcs we do not make clear just

---

*Suggested by Professor Norman Anning of the University of Michigan.

which arcs we mean, but this is relatively unimportant since corresponding arcs are equal all around.

Pages 147-152: Exercises.

1. The sum of two opposite angles of the quadrilateral is equal to half the sum of two central angles that add up to $360°$.

3. In Fig. 24 $\angle ABC = 90° = \angle ABD$, so CBD is a straight line.

4. For the left-hand figure:

$\angle C + \angle ABD = 180°$ and

$\angle ABD + \angle ABF = 180°$.

Therefore $\angle C = \angle ABF$

$\angle ABF + \angle E = 180°$.

Therefore $\angle C + \angle E = 180°$ and chords CD and EF are parallel (by page 110, lines 1-3).

For the right-hand figure:

$\angle C + \angle ABD = 180°$ and $\angle AEF + \angle ABD = 180°$.

Therefore $\angle C = \angle AEF$ and chords CD and EF are parallel.

5. $\angle APC = \angle B + \angle C = \frac{1}{2} \angle AOC + \frac{1}{2} \angle BOD = \frac{1}{2}(\angle AOC + \angle BOD)$, where O is the center of the circle.

6. $\angle APC = \angle ABC - \angle BCD = \frac{1}{2} \angle AOC - \frac{1}{2} \angle BOD = \frac{1}{2}(\angle AOC - \angle BOD)$

7. Draw the bisector OM of the isosceles triangle TOB (Fig. 28) and prove that two angles at M are right angles. It follows that angle MOT and the angle between the tangent and the chord are both equal to $90° - \angle MTO$.

9. Use the fact that the four angles of quadrilateral PSOT add up to $360°$ and that two of these angles are right angles.

10. From Ex. 9 $\angle SPT = 180°$ - the lesser angle SOT =

$\frac{1}{2}(360°$ - twice the lesser angle SOT) =

$\frac{1}{2}$(greater angle SOT + lesser angle SOT - 2 · lesser angle SOT) =

$\frac{1}{2}$(greater angle SOT - lesser angle SOT).

- 93 -

11. $63\frac{1}{2}^{\circ}$

12. $180^{\circ} - 120\frac{1}{2}^{\circ} = 59\frac{1}{2}^{\circ}$

13. 69°

14. Note that Exs. 14, 17, 23, 24, and 25 say "show" - not "prove" - and "can be regarded." All that is expected of the student in these five exercises is an intuitive recognition of limiting cases.

   In Fig. 26, as D approaches B, $\angle$ C approaches 0° and $\angle$ APC approaches $\angle$ B + 0°.

15. $27\frac{1}{2}^{\circ}$

16. 34°

17. See note on Ex. 14.

   In Fig. 27, as D approaches B, $\angle$ BCD approaches 0° and $\angle$ APC approaches $\angle$ ABC - 0°.

18. In Fig. 28, when $\angle$ TOB = 90°, $\angle$ OTB = 45° = the angle between tangent and chord. When $\angle$ TOB = 180°, TB is a diameter and is perpendicular to the tangent at T.

19. $12\frac{1}{2}^{\circ}$

20. 52°

21. 43°

22. 222.2° and 137.8°

23. See note on Ex. 14.

24. See note on Ex. 14.

   As B moves along the circle toward T, P moves toward T along the tangent and $\angle$ PAT approaches 0°.

25. See note on Ex. 14.

   Let A and B withdraw from T along the circle until A and B approach coincidence.

27. Use Corollary 22c and Ex. 15, page 86.

28. $2\sqrt{3}$

29. $\frac{13}{4}$

30. In Fig. 31, let DO = x. Then AD = 4 - x, DB = 4 + x, and $(PD)^2 = 9 =$
    $(4 - x)(4 + x) = 16 - x^2$. Therefore $x^2 = 7$ and $x = \sqrt{7}$.

    Alternative solution: Let AD = x. Then DB = 8 - x and $(PD)^2 = 9 =$
    $x(8 - x) = 8x - x^2$ and $x^2 - 8x + 9 = 0$. Using the quadratic formula,
    $x = 4 \stackrel{+}{-} \sqrt{7}$.

31. PA = $2\sqrt{6}$ and PB = $2\sqrt{10}$

32. PA = 4 and PB = $4\sqrt{3}$

33. AB = 6 and PB = $3\sqrt{3}$

34. AD = $\frac{8}{\sqrt{13}}$ and PD = $\frac{12}{\sqrt{13}}$

37. $\angle$ PTA = $\angle$ PBT; therefore triangles PTA and PBT are similar.

38. Use Ex. 37.

39. $\frac{20}{7}$

40. 7.4

41. $\frac{77}{6}$

42. Letting CP = x, we have $x^2 + 5x = 96$. The teacher should tell the
    pupil in advance that he will meet an equation of this sort and will
    be expected to find an approximate solution by trial-and-error. For
    example, 7 is too small, and 8 is too large; $7\frac{1}{2}$ seems about right;
    try it. We get $56 + \frac{1}{4} + 37 + \frac{1}{2} = 93\frac{3}{4}$, which is a bit small. So
    we try 7.6, getting 57.76 + 38.0 = 95.76, and this is very close
    indeed.

    Applying the quadratic formula to the equation $x^2 + 5x - 96 = 0$
    yields $x = \frac{-5 + \sqrt{409}}{2} = 7.6$ and another value that we reject because
    it is negative.

43. $2\sqrt{15}$

44. Letting AP = x, we have $x^2 + 4x = 64$. The teacher should tell the
    pupil in advance that he will meet an equation of this sort and will
    be expected to find an approximate solution by trial-and-error. For

example, 6 is too small and 7 is too large; $6\frac{1}{4}$ seems about right; try it. We get $(6 + \frac{1}{4})^2 + 4(\frac{25}{4}) = 36 + 3 + \frac{1}{16} + 25 = 64\frac{1}{16}$. So $6\frac{1}{4}$ is very close indeed.

Applying the quadratic formula to the equation $x^2 + 4x - 64 = 0$ yields $x = 2\sqrt{17} - 2 = 6.24$ and another value that we reject because it is negative.

45. 56.25

47. See note on Ex. 14.

In Fig. 33, let A and B move toward each other along the minor arc AB; then let C and D move toward each other along the minor arc CD. In the case that both secants become tangents we have the situation in Ex. 8 on page 141.

Page 152: In Theorem 23 the fussiest point of the proof concerns a detail that is of least interest to the pupil, namely, whether PM and QN intersect or not.

Pages 154-155: Exercises.

1. The first two paragraphs of the proof of Theorem 23 on page 153 can be applied to any triangle ABC.

2. In Fig. 36, triangles OAB and OBC are equal isosceles triangles; so ∠ABO = ∠CBO.

3. If we regard Fig. 36 as representing part of an inscribed equilateral polygon, the equality of the base angles of the several equal isosceles triangles is sufficient to prove that ∠A = ∠B = ∠C = ∠D = ... Thus the definition of regular polygon on page 85 is satisfied.

If the equilateral polygon is formed by joining every second, or every third, or every fourth, ..., point of division on the circle, then the polygon will be a star when n is odd.

4. See Figs. A and B on the next page.

Fig. A

Fig. B

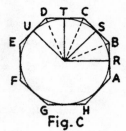

Fig. C

5. In Fig. C, polygon ABCDEFGH is equi-angular. The inscribed circle touches the sides of the polygon at R, S, T, U, ... so that triangles ROB, BOS, SOC, COT, ... are similar. For the angles at R, S, T, U, ... are right angles (Theorem 21) and the angles at B, C, D, ... are halves of equal angles. These triangles are also equal, since OR = OS = OT = OU = ... Therefore RB = BS = SC = CT = TD = ..., and BC = CD = ..., so that ABCDEFGH is a regular polygon.

6. See Figs. D and E below.

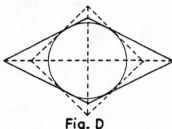

Fig. D

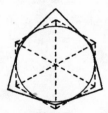

Fig. E

7. Since each angle of the polygon is measured by (see footnote on page 145) the same number of equal arcs, all the angles of the polygon are equal. The sides are all equal also (Theorem 19).

In Ex. 7 and Ex. 8 the phrase "any number" means "any integer greater than two."

- 97 -

8. If the chords are drawn also, as in Ex. 7, we have n isosceles triangles. In each triangle the angle between tangent and chord is the
same, so that the triangles are similar isosceles triangles. Therefore the angles at the vertices of the circumscribed polygon are all
equal. Since the chords are all equal, these isosceles triangles
are not only similar, but equal; so that the sides of the circumscribed polygon are all equal.

9. One method of proof follows the pattern of the proof in Ex. 8, showing first that the isosceles triangles are all similar, and then
that they are all equal.

   A second method is merely to apply the theorem in Ex. 7 on this
page.

   That the number of sides is doubled is sufficiently obvious without
expecting the student to give a formal proof.

10. This can be proved either by drawing chords and considering the
isosceles triangles, as in Exs. 8 and 9, or by immediate application
of the theorem in Ex. 8 on this page.

11. Prove angles equal by Ex. 6 on page 85. Since $AB = BC = CD = \ldots$
and $A'B' = B'C' = C'D' = \ldots$, $\dfrac{AB}{A'B'} = \dfrac{BC}{B'C'} = \dfrac{CD}{C'D'} = \ldots$

12. $\dfrac{5}{\sqrt{2}}$

13. $7\sqrt{2}$

14. $\dfrac{4}{\sqrt{3}}$

15. $7\sqrt{3}$

16. $30\sqrt{3}$

Pages 157-161: Exercises.

1. $\angle SRT = \frac{1}{2}\angle O$

   $\angle RST = \frac{1}{2}\angle O'$

   $\angle SRT + \angle RST = \frac{1}{2}(\angle O + \angle O') = \frac{1}{2}(180^\circ)$

   Therefore $\angle RTS = 90^\circ$.

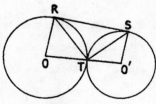

Fig. A

2. It is necessary only to prove that the marked angles in each of the diagrams below are equal.

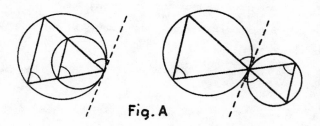

Fig. A

3. Use the preceding exercise and also Ex. 5 on page 127.

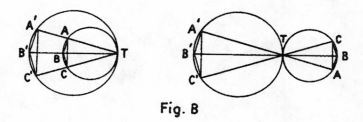

Fig. B

4. In Fig. C, TA' and TB' are random chords through T. It is sufficient to prove by Ex. 2 on this page that chords AB and A'B' are parallel.

5. See Fig. D. In each case ∠ ATB = 90°. Therefore ∠ A'TB' = 90° also, and A'B' is a diameter.

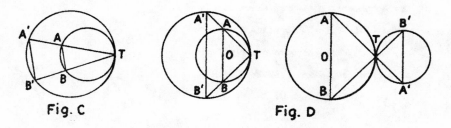

Fig. C   Fig. D

6. It is not necessary that all pupils suggest the same property. This is an interesting and significant diagram, and the total of all correct

suggestions will enlighten everyone. There are times when the teacher will prefer to ask "see what you can discover" rather than "see if you can see what the book says you should see."

See Fig. A below. P is equidistant from R, S, and T; Q is equidistant from U, V, and T.

PQ = RS = UV. For PT = $\frac{1}{2}$RS; QT = $\frac{1}{2}$UV; and RS = UV because RM = UM and SM = VM.

7. Use the theorem in Ex. 37 on page 151.

8. See Fig. B. Triangle ADO is a 30° - 60° right triangle. Therefore DO = $\frac{1}{2}$AO = $\frac{1}{2}$CO, and DO = $\frac{1}{3}$DC.

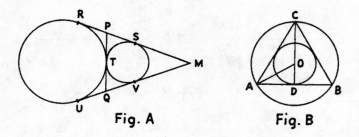

Fig. A   Fig. B

9. Since the inscribed angles C and D are measured by one half the same arcs respectively, however CD may be drawn, the sizes of these two angles do not vary. Consequently angle DBC does not vary in size.

10. The accompanying diagram shows circles O and Q of Fig. 41, to which the lines OA, QE, OQ, and the common tangent ST at C have been added. By Ex. 16 on page 143 OQ passes through C. Since ∠ TCA = ∠ SCE, $\frac{1}{2}$∠AOC = $\frac{1}{2}$ ∠ EQC and OA is parallel to QE. Similarly, in Fig. 41, PA is parallel to QD. But OAP is a straight line. Therefore EQD is straight also.

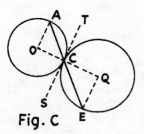

Fig. C

11. In Fig. 42 the angles at A and B are complementary. If the other
    tangents from A and B are drawn, these angles at A and B will be
    doubled; that is, they will be supplementary, and the new tangents
    will be parallel.

12. The lengths of the segments in question are either the sum or
    difference of equal tangents from an external point.

13. If we letter the arcs a, b, c, d, e, ... in order, then in the
    case of the equiangular polygon of five sides the equality of the
    angles tells us that $a + b + c = b + c + d = c + d + e = d + e + a =$
    $e + a + b = a + b + c$. It follows that $a = d$, $b = e$, $c = a$, $d = b$,
    $e = c$, and hence that $a = b = c = d = e$. Since this polygon is both
    equilateral and equiangular, it is regular.

    If the equiangular polygon has six sides, we get $a + b + c + d =$
    $b + c + d + e = c + d + e + f = d + e + f + a = e + f + a + b =$
    $f + a + b + c = a + b + c + d$. It follows that $a = e$, $b = f$, $c = a$,
    $d = b$, $e = c$, $f = d$ and hence that $a = c = e$ and $b = d = f$; but there
    is no way of equating a, c, or e to b, d, or f.

    If the equiangular polygon has seven sides, we get $a = f$, $b = g$,
    $c = a$, $d = b$, $e = c$, $f = d$, $g = e$. This is like the series of equa-
    tions for the pentagon, except that in each equation we now skip four
    letters instead of two. Since in each of these two cases the total
    number of letters is odd, this skipping of an even number of letters
    links all the letters and equations together. The same is true of any
    polygon having an odd number of sides. Whereas in the case of any
    polygon having an even number of sides, like the hexagon, we skip an
    odd number of letters in each equation of the series; and since the
    total number of letters is even, we succeed in linking only half the
    letters into one series of equations, and the other half into a sec-
    ond series of equations; we can never bring the two series together.

- 101 -

14. In the case of the equilateral polygon of five
sides, or of any odd number of sides, the segments of the tangents are equal in pairs around
the polygon, as marked, beginning at vertex A,
until there is overlap; that is, until an <u>a</u>
segment is seen to be equal to a <u>b</u> segment.
Consequently each vertex of the polygon is at

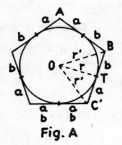

Fig. A

the same distance r' from the center of the given circle (Principle 12)
and the polygon can be inscribed in a circle of radius r'. By Ex. 3
on page 154 the polygon is regular.

Or, having proved an <u>a</u> segment equal to a <u>b</u> segment, we can prove
∠ OBT equal to ∠ OCT, and hence ∠ B = ∠ C. In this way the equilateral polygon is proved to be equiangular also, and therefore regular.

In case the circumscribed equilateral polygon has an even number
of sides, the segments of the tangents are equal in pairs but without
overlap. It is impossible to prove that the polygon is regular.
Ex. 6 on page 155 affords examples of circumscribed equilateral
polygons that are not regular.

15. In Fig. 43, AO · OB = CO · OD;

$$AO · OB = EO · OP;$$

$$CO · OD = EO · OQ;$$

therefore OP = OQ.

Note: Exs. 16-23, like the other exercises on three-dimensional
geometry in this book, are not meant to be logically connected with
the two-dimensional geometry. They are included principally to challenge the pupil's imagination.

16. A circle. It is assumed, of course, that the pupil will think only
of a right circular cone. To include a technical phrase of this sort
in the question would add mystery rather than clarity.

17. A circle. Here also it is assumed that the pupil will consider only a right circular cylinder.

   The coin must be held horizontal; parallel to the tilted cover. The coin will cast an elliptic shadow if the plane of the coin is not parallel to the floor (cover) and does not contain the perpendicular from the light to the floor (cover). In the latter case the shadow would be a "broad" line segment.

18. Circle. Meridian and equator are equal circles. Centers of all great circles are at the center of the sphere. Parallels of latitude are smaller circles than "great circles" and diminish as the latitude increases from equator to pole. The centers of all these circles are on the axis joining the two poles of the sphere.

19. The center of the sphere and the two given points on the surface of the sphere ordinarily determine a plane. This plane intersects the sphere in a great circle. Three points in a straight line do not "determine" a plane: this line can lie in a multitude of planes. This situation arises when the two given points are the extremities of a diameter. For example, there are a multitude of meridians through the north and south poles of the earth.

20. Cape Race, Newfoundland; Southern Ireland.

21. 75° in both cases

22. 5 hours. The sun's apparent motion around the earth covers 360 degrees in 24 hours; that is, 15 degrees in 1 hour.

23. One equilateral spherical triangle that is likely to occur to the student is the triangle each of whose sides is a quadrant (90°) of a great circle. If such a triangle be drawn on a tennis ball and then an equilateral triangle with shorter sides - say 60° - be drawn inside the first triangle, the angles of the second triangle will obviously be smaller than the 90° angles of the first triangle.

Pages 161-163: Exercises.

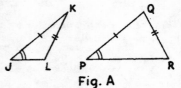
Fig. A

1. It does not follow; for consider the triangles shown in Fig. A, in which JK = PQ, KL = QR, and ∠ J = ∠ P.

2. To say "draw FM parallel to CD" demands too much. Either one should draw a line through F parallel to CD and then prove that it meets ED at M; or else draw FM and prove that FM is parallel to CD.

3. This is a case of "begging the question"; for the idea of equally distant lines has no meaning for the student without the idea of parallelism and so cannot be used in a definition of parallelism.

4. If it is reasonable to expect a team to win a majority of its games, is it not equally reasonable that each of its opponents should expect to win a majority of its games?

5. Are there any limits to the right of the taxpayers to see their property?

6. It is necessary to know first how many heat units one ton of gas works' coke yields. If it yields at least 9900 heat units per ton, the Seacoal salesman's argument is worthless.

7. Or else the public school graduates do their college work more faithfully than do the private school graduates. There may be economic and social reasons for this, quite apart from the earlier training in school subjects.

8. Despite Blank's mistake, as he called it, he seems to have been very successful in the world of business.

9. It is assumed that a self-emptying ash tray is an important enough item to determine the choice of an automobile.

10. It is assumed that men's choices determine styles, rather than the other way around.

11. It is assumed that the usual risk in a new business venture is not very great.

12. It is assumed that the prosperity referred to was attributable to the party in power rather than to economic forces that would have been operating regardless of party politics.

13. It is assumed that those whose taxes remain unpaid for several years are poor widows and the like.

C H A P T E R 6

Constructions with straightedge and compasses are not necessary to
BASIC GEOMETRY.* Other geometries are plagued by the necessity of demon-
strating the existence of midpoints of line-segments, bisectors of angles, and the like before they may make use of these points and lines.
They are plagued also by the necessity of showing how these midpoints and
bisecting lines can be constructed, using only the two instruments to
which Euclid and his successors decided to restrict themselves. The
authors of other geometries have always been embarrassed if they felt
obliged to employ the bisector of the vertex angle of an isosceles triangle in order to prove the equality of the angles opposite the equal
sides. For they planned to use this theorem about isosceles triangles
in order to prove the equality of triangles having mutually equal sides,
and they required this latter theorem in turn to support the construction
for the bisector of an angle: obviously a "vicious circle."

In most geometries logic demands demonstrations of constructibility
in advance of use. But it is impossible to provide for the construction
of every point and line in advance of its use in the logical deduction of a

*See Chapter 2, page 39, of this manual.

geometric system without seriously upsetting the system. BASIC GEOMETRY, on the other hand, is so designed as to be free of this logical compulsion; for in BASIC GEOMETRY the existence of required points and lines is established by the fundamental assumptions, or by propositions derivable therefrom. Other geometries have usually deemed it better not to allow the need of fundamental constructions to derange their logical system too seriously. They have usually preferred to save a semblance of order in the geometric system by taking a few fundamental constructions for granted at the outset, and - if challenged - by admitting the lapse in logic required by these "hypothetical constructions."

BASIC GEOMETRY is quite untroubled by considerations of this sort. Principles 1 and 3 imply the existence of the midpoint of a line-segment and the existence of a half-line that bisects an angle. The existence of other geometric configurations required in this geometry is demonstrated as the geometry develops. Strictly, all of BASIC GEOMETRY is developed in the realm of the imagination. The marked ruler and protractor, however, afford practical embodiment of Principles 1 and 3 for those who wish actually "to go through the motions." The authors themselves quite approve of every effort to give practical effect to this system of geometry through free use of the marked ruler, the protractor, and the compasses. But they would make clear that their interest in constructions is based on obvious educational considerations and is not required by this system of geometry itself. Put in another way, it can be said that BASIC GEOMETRY was intentionally devised to be susceptible of immediate interpretation by means of scale and protractor, but that its logical structure is independent of such interpretation and application. That is why the authors of BASIC GEOMETRY have had no qualms about developing the bulk of this geometry before considering constructions at all. That, too, is why they did not need to scatter constructions through the

- 107 -

earlier chapters of this book, but could present all the material on constructions in one chapter and could put this chapter as late as they chose.

Now that the subject of constructions is at last before us, the authors insist that only the marked ruler, the protractor, and compasses are necessary. But the question of limiting geometric constructions still further to those constructions that can be performed by unmarked straightedge and compasses has been regarded as a part of geometry for so long a time that the authors of BASIC GEOMETRY would not omit consideration of this problem. Constructions with straightedge and compasses are logically not a part of BASIC GEOMETRY; at this point they are indeed a digression. But the authors of BASIC GEOMETRY recognize the fascinating geometric content of this subject and, with this explanation, welcome this digression.

Page 168, line 5: 1.4 inches

Pages 169-170: Exercises.

1. The length of CD is a trifle more than 5 centimeters and a trifle less than 2 inches. It is easier to lay off 1 centimeter "plus a hair" than to lay off $\frac{2}{5}$ of an inch "minus a hair." Nevertheless with a scale of inches divided to sixteenths the student can approximate to $\frac{2}{5}$ of an inch. He must not collapse and quit because he hasn't a scale divided precisely into fifths or tenths of inches. This question, therefore, is to some extent a test of the student's initiative and resourcefulness.

2. The length of EF is a scant $2\frac{3}{4}$ inches, or 6.96 centimeters. The latter is more easily divided by 6. Indeed the decision to call the length 6.96 centimeters rather than 6.95 or 6.97 is influenced by the desired divisibility by 6.

3. 3.737, 4.010, 4.283

4. If $\frac{1}{m} = \frac{3}{2}$, merely use the third point of division in the answer to
   Ex. 1.

5. Using millimeters, r:s:t = 36:28:20 = 9:7:5. So we need to lay off
   $\frac{3}{7}$, $\frac{1}{3}$, $\frac{5}{21}$ of 7 centimeters, scant.

6. $\frac{14}{9}$ centimeters

7. 5.0(4) centimeters

8. ∠ AOB = 63°. Each third is 21°.

9. ∠ COD = 94°; ∠ EOF = 29°. The two parts are approximately 48° and 15°

10. About $43\frac{1}{2}°$

11-12. Use method described on page 168.

   Page 171, lines 20-25, are an intentional repetition of lines 8-13
on page 166.

   Pages 171-172: Exercises.

1. Make angles of 135° at each end of AB and lay off lengths BC and AH
   equal to AB; and so on around.

2. Make angles of 140° at each end of AB and lay off lengths BC and AI
   equal to AB; and so on around.

3-4. Central angles must be 45° and 40° respectively.

   Page 173, line 9. See note in this manual relating to Exs. 13-15
on pages 142, 143 of BASIC GEOMETRY. Euclid, using in his Proposition 1
a construction similar to the one shown in Fig. 17 on page 172, failed
to demonstrate that the two circles must have at least one point in common; and if one, then two.

   Page 175. The third method described here involves fewer operations
than any other construction known to the authors for drawing through a
given point a line that is parallel to a given line. Their knowledge
of it is due to their colleague J. L. Coolidge, who attributes it to the
Italian mathematician, Mascheroni (pronounced Maskeroni).

   Page 176, line 10. In any pair of triangles Principle 5 establishes pairs of corresponding angles equal. These equal angles establish the parallelism, by Theorem 14.

Page 176, lines 14-16. Draw parallels to BS through P, Q, and R. Proof of the construction depends on Theorem 16.

Page 178, line 8. By Ex. 21 on page 115.

Page 178, line 12. Proof depends on Ex. 20 on page 115.

Page 178, line 18. Proof depends on Principle 8.

Page 180, lines 9 and 20. Note three ways of writing the mean proportional relation.

Pages 180-181: Exercises.

1. Construct the perpendicular bisector of the chord of the arc and find where it intersects the arc.

2. Draw the perpendicular through E to AB and find where the perpendicular intersects the diagonal AC.

3. $\sqrt{7}$ is the diagonal of a square of side $\sqrt{3.5}$.

At this point the teacher may wish to show the class the accompanying construction for $\sqrt{k}$:

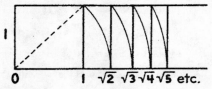

Fig. A

4. The unit of measure is not specified, since it makes no difference what the unit is.

5. Fig. 28 involves three equilateral triangles. Fig. 29 involves a triangle having one angle equal to 60° and the sides including this angle in the ratio 2:1. Fig. 30 involves an angle inscribed in a semicircle. See Corollary 22c, page 146.

Page 183, line 7. Note that we do not ask for proof here, although all that is needed is Principle 9 and Ex. 13 on page 85, as indicated in the footnote on page 182. The proof is demanded later, in Ex. 19, page 256.

Page 185, line 10. OP and O'R are both perpendicular to the required

common internal tangent PR. A parallel through O' to PR will be perpendicular to OP extended and will meet it at M. O'M will then be tangent
at M to the circle having O as center and radius equal to OP + PM, or
r + r'.

Page 185, line 14. We use the word "sides" here to denote lengths,
just as elsewhere on occasion we have used "altitude" and "radius" to
denote lengths.

Page 186, line 22: Case 2. At one end of a line segment of length $\underline{1}$
construct an angle equal to ∠A or to ∠B. At the other end of the line
segment construct an angle equal to ∠C by first constructing an exterior
angle equal to ∠A + ∠B. See Fig. A. There are two cases, according as
side $\underline{1}$ is given opposite angle B or opposite angle A.

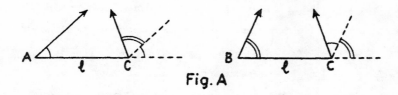

Fig. A

Page 186, line 25 and Page 187, line 4. The student must observe
that the given situation varies according to the size of the given angle A
and according to the relative size of l and m. The authors want the student to figure out for himself how many different situations can occur.
They prefer the student's possibly incomplete appraisal based on his own
inquiry to a complete appraisal arrived at merely by filling in a table
or following a procedure outlined in the book.

Page 188, line 3. The fifth and sixth situations in Fig. 46 on
page 187.

Whether the dotted right triangle shown in the seventh situation in
Fig. 46 is admissible or not can open a long argument. The question is,
can the dotted triangle be said to contain the given angle A, or is this
a third case in which "two triangles seem at first to be possible; but

closer examination shows that one triangle contains, not angle A, but an angle equal to 180° - A"? The important thing is to have the pupils discuss this, no matter how they decide it.

Page 188, Ex. 2. Let the pupils discover for themselves the best places to put the flaps. This calls for a bit of three-dimensional visualization of a sort we wish to encourage. If a pupil discovers on his first attempt that he is trying to fit two sticky flaps down inside two faces at the same time and then pushes the flaps in a bit too far, it may occur to him to make a second attempt, with the flaps attached to the receiving faces, leaving the folding face unflapped. The drawing is so easy that it is no hardship to be obliged to make a second one, especially if the pupil learns something in the process.

Page 191, line 11. Most students will be interested to know this simple construction for an inscribed regular pentagon. Relatively few will wish to master the details of the proof on page 192, 193.

Page 194, line 7. Professor Norman Anning of the University of Michigan points out that the circle with center C and radius CH (Fig. 54) cuts the given circle in two vertices of an inscribed regular pentagon; that the circle with center C and radius CK cuts the given circle in two more vertices of this same pentagon; and that the fifth vertex is given by the other end of the diameter through C.

Page 195, line 3. For proof that it is impossible in general to trisect an angle by means of straightedge and compasses see L. E. Dickson, First Course in the Theory of Equations, Chapter 3, pages 29-35, John Wiley and Sons, New York, 1922.

Pages 195-196: Exercises.

1. Construct tangents to the circle at the vertices of an inscribed regular hexagon and extend these tangents until they meet (the bisectors of the central angles of the hexagon).

3. Trisect a right angle and bisect one of the 30° angles.

4. Inscribe a regular polygon of 15 sides and bisect a central angle. Then bisect again.

5. Inscribe a regular pentagon. The radius drawn to a vertex makes an angle of $54°$ with each adjacent side of the pentagon.

6. $108°$

7. Construct an angle of $108°$ by drawing a circle of any radius and inscribing a regular pentagon. Then, at each end of the given side AB construct an angle equal to $108°$. And so on around.

8. At each end of the given side AB construct an angle of $135°$, presumably by erecting perpendiculars at A and B and bisecting the right angle between each perpendicular and AB extended.

9. As in Ex. 7.

10. From one vertex of the given polygon draw n-3 diagonals and copy the appropriate angles. This is easier than using the construction for the fourth proportional to three given line segments.

11. In equilateral triangle ABC (Fig. A), construct the three medians, meeting in O. The bisector of angle BFO will meet BO at a point G that is equidistant from BD, BF, DO, and FO. Therefore G is the center of one of the desired circles. Another and much harder method is to mark off on BO the distance BG equal to $\dfrac{AB}{\sqrt{3}+1}$.

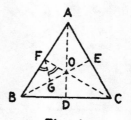

Fig. A

12. Draw the diagonals of the square. The midpoint of each half of a diagonal will be the center of one of the desired circles.

13. In the given square ABCD (see Fig. A on the next page) draw the diagonals AC and BD, meeting at O. Construct the bisectors of angles OAB and OBA. These bisectors meet at Q, the center of one of the desired circles.

A slightly easier construction, but somewhat harder to justify, is to draw the diagonals AC and BD, meeting at O; draw arcs with centers C and D and radii CO and DO respectively to determine the points E, F, G, and H and thus determine the intersection R of EF and GH. R is the center of one of the desired circles. For if the side of the given square be $\underline{s}$ and if the radius of one of the desired circles be $\underline{r}$, then Fig. B shows that $\frac{s}{2} = r + r\sqrt{2}$. But Fig. B also shows that if $\underline{t}$ be one side of the regular octagon GFIH - - -, then $\frac{s}{2} = \frac{t}{2} + \frac{t}{\sqrt{2}} = \frac{t}{2}(1 + \sqrt{2})$. Consequently $r = \frac{t}{2}$ and we can utilize the regular octagon to locate the centers of the desired circles.

It is clear from Fig. A that $DO = DG = DH = \frac{s}{\sqrt{2}}$ and that $DG + FC = s + FG$. That is, $2\left(\frac{s}{\sqrt{2}}\right) = s + FG$ and $FG = s(\sqrt{2} - 1)$. But $s = t + 2\left(\frac{t}{\sqrt{2}}\right) = t(1 + \sqrt{2})$, and $t = \frac{s}{\sqrt{2} + 1} = s(\sqrt{2} - 1)$. Therefore $FG = t$.

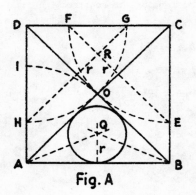
Fig. A

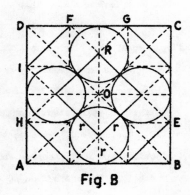
Fig. B

15. The single-marked flaps should be pasted first, then the double-marked flaps. The face marked L will be the last to be stuck down. See Fig. A at the top of page 115.

16. First draw a random circle, inscribe a regular pentagon ABCDE, and draw diagonal AC. Then at each end of the given line-segment A'C' construct an angle equal to angle BAC and thus determine B'.

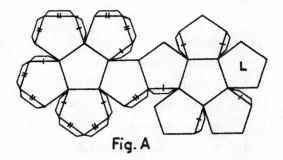

Fig. A

If instead of using angles one wishes to use lengths, it is necessary to note that all the acute-angled triangles formed by the sides
and diagonals of a regular pentagon are isosceles triangles with
angles 72°-36°-72°. In
every triangle of this
sort, such as triangle
FBG in Fig. B, the short
side is to one of the
longer sides as $\sqrt{5} - 1$ is
to 2. (See page 192). If

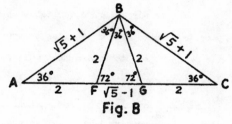

Fig. B

we take FG as $\sqrt{5} - 1$ and BF as 2, then AF = GC = 2; AB = AG = $\sqrt{5} + 1$;
and AC = $\sqrt{5} + 3$. So the ratio of the desired length AB to the given
length AC is as $\sqrt{5} + 1$ is to $\sqrt{5} + 3$.

17. If r be the radius of the given circle, draw a circle with center O
    that shall have a radius equal to $\sqrt{r^2 + 1^2}$. This circle will cut
    the given line in two points from either of which tangents to the
    given circle will be of length 1.

There is no summary at the end of this chapter because, as already
explained, this chapter is not part of the logical framework of BASIC
GEOMETRY. The main outline of this geometry is given in the summaries of
Chapters 2, 3, 4, 5, and 7.

C H A P T E R 7

The title of this chapter means "area of any closed figure lying in one plane, and the length of an arc of a circle." Except for the idea of length of a straight line segment, with which this geometry begins, the idea of length in general is much more difficult than the idea of area. That is why this chapter takes up first the subject of area, and why it is able to extend the idea of area to any plane figure whatsoever while being unable to extend the idea of length, beyond the straight line, to any plane curve except the simplest case of all, the circle.

Page 198, line 17, and **Page 199, line 16**. One can say that for the beginner this geometry requires five assumptions (Principles 1-5), plus five more tentative assumptions (Principles 6, 7, 8, 11 and Theorem 13), plus two area assumptions: that is, twelve assumptions in all. Actually, however, this geometry requires only four assumptions, since Principle 4 has been shown to be a theorem (See BASIC GEOMETRY, page 50, and this manual, pages 46-47), and since area can be treated, as shown on page 222, so as to require no new assumptions.

Page 199, line 8. The word "unit" is not defined in this book. However, the second paragraph on page 40 implies that different units of length are associated with different modes of numbering the points of a straight line.

Page 199: Exercises.

1. 137 square units

1. In the similar triangles ABC and CBE,

   $\frac{AC}{AB} = \frac{CE}{BC}$. Therefore $\frac{1}{2}$AC x BC = $\frac{1}{2}$AB x CE.

2. See Fig. A. The area of a rectangle

   ABFG = AB x CE. But, since $\triangle$ ACE = $\triangle$ ACG

   and $\triangle$ BCE = $\triangle$ BCF, the area of triangle

   ABC is half the area of rectangle ABFG.

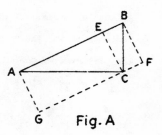

Fig. A

Page 201: Theorem 26. If D falls to the left of A in Fig. 3 on page

201, the given triangle is equal to one in which D falls to the right of

C. Of course, if D falls on C or on A we have the right triangle case

covered in Theorem 25.

Pages 202-203: Exercises.

1. 905 square units, where the unit of area is one of the smallest

   squares of the squared paper. This can be found either by assigning

   coordinates to each vertex of the diagram as in Ex. 1 on page 199, or

   by counting the number of squares inside the boundary.

2-3. The area of the left-hand triangle in Fig. 3 is $\frac{1}{2}$ x $\frac{26}{16}$ in. x $\frac{8\frac{1}{2}}{16}$ in. =

   $\frac{1}{2}$ x $\frac{221}{256}$ sq. in., using $\frac{1}{2}$AC x BD; or $\frac{1}{2}$ x $\frac{20\frac{1}{2}}{16}$ in. x $\frac{11}{16}$ in. = $\frac{1}{2}$ x $\frac{225\frac{1}{2}}{256}$ sq.

   in., using $\frac{1}{2}$AB times the altitude from C. In either case the area is

   approximately $\frac{7}{16}$ of a square inch. The area of the right-hand tri-

   angle is $\frac{1}{2}$ x $\frac{18\frac{1}{2}}{16}$ in. x $\frac{1}{2}$ in. = $\frac{37}{128}$ sq. in., using $\frac{1}{2}$AC x BD; or

   $\frac{1}{2}$ x $\frac{26}{16}$ in. x $\frac{3}{8}$ in. = $\frac{39}{128}$ sq. in., using $\frac{1}{2}$AB times the altitude from C.

   In either case the area is approximately $\frac{19}{64}$ of a square inch.

4. 29 millimeters x 17 millimeters = 493 sq. mm., or $\frac{18}{16}$ in. x $\frac{10\frac{1}{2}}{16}$ in. =

   $\frac{189}{256}$ sq. in. = 0.738 sq. in.

5. Area equals $\frac{\frac{1}{2}(29 + 10\frac{1}{2})}{16}$ in. x $\frac{1}{2}$ in. = $\frac{79}{128}$ sq. in., or about $\frac{5}{8}$ of

   a square inch.

6. $\frac{s^2}{4}\sqrt{3}$

7. $e^2\sqrt{3}$

8. Add the area of the three parallelogram faces to the area of both

triangular bases. If the prism is a right prism, the three faces are rectangles, and their area is equal to the altitude of the prism times the perimeter of one of the triangular bases.

9. $\frac{\frac{1}{2}bh}{\frac{1}{2}b'h'} = \frac{b \cdot b}{b' \cdot b'}$, since $\frac{h}{h'} = \frac{a}{a'} = \frac{b}{b'} = \frac{c}{c'}$

10. $\frac{\triangle ABC}{\triangle ADC} = \frac{\frac{1}{2}AB \times h}{\frac{1}{2}AD \times h} = \frac{AB}{AD}$; also $\frac{\triangle ADC}{\triangle ADE} = \frac{\frac{1}{2}AC \times h'}{\frac{1}{2}AE \times h'} = \frac{AC}{AE}$. Multiplying,

we get $\frac{\triangle ABC}{\triangle ADE} = \frac{AB \times AC}{AD \times AE}$.

Pages 204-205: Exercises.

2. Apothem = $\frac{5}{2}\sqrt{3}$ inches; area = $\frac{75}{2}\sqrt{3}$ square inches

3. Area = $\frac{3}{2}\sqrt{3} \, r^2$

4. Perimeter = $3\sqrt{3} \, r$; area = $\frac{3}{4}\sqrt{3} \, r^2$

5. Apothem = $\frac{s}{2\sqrt{3}}$; radius = $\frac{s}{\sqrt{3}}$

6. On page 193 the apothem $r - y$ is shown to be $r\left(\frac{1 + \sqrt{5}}{4}\right)$. Therefore

the area is $\frac{5}{2} \cdot \frac{r}{2}\sqrt{10 - 2\sqrt{5}} \cdot \frac{r}{4} (1 + \sqrt{5})$. This equals

$\frac{5}{16} r^2 \sqrt{(10 - 2\sqrt{5})(6 + 2\sqrt{5})}$, or $\frac{5}{8} r^2 \sqrt{10 + 2\sqrt{5}}$.

7. Using the measurements shown in the accompanying diagrams, the area of the left-hand polygon is 455 sq. mm. and the area of the right-hand polygon is 456 sq. mm. The numbers inside the triangles are altitudes.

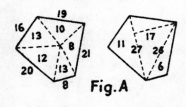

Fig. A

8. Counting <u>up</u>, we have 20 + 108 + 120 + 110 + 93 = 451 sq. mm.

9. Counting from left to right we have 48 + 105 + 103 + 65 + 40 + 49 + 70 + 61 + 2 = 543 sq. mm.

10. If the lengths of the sides of the given polygons are s_1 and s_2 respectively, then $\frac{p_1}{p_2} = \frac{s_1}{s_2} = \frac{r_1}{r_2}$.

11. From Ex. 1 and Ex. 10 we know that $\dfrac{A_1}{A_2} = \dfrac{\frac{1}{2}p_1 a_1}{\frac{1}{2}p_2 a_2} = \dfrac{r_1 a_1}{r_2 a_2}$

Therefore $\dfrac{A_1}{A_2} = \dfrac{r_1^2}{r_2^2}$.

Page 206, line 9. The letter k is used here in the same way as in Ex. 37 on page 66, referred to farther down on page 206. It is possible, however, that some students will confuse this k with the k used in Principle 5 on page 59. In that case they would have expected to see the k on page 206 replaced by $\dfrac{1}{k^2}$. The teacher should explain that it is quite immaterial whether we use k or k^2 or $\dfrac{1}{k}$ or $\dfrac{1}{k^2}$ here to represent the ratio of the areas of these two triangles.

Pages 207-208: Exercises.

1. 1 to 400

2. $\dfrac{81}{64}$

3. It is assumed in this exercise, of course, that the three sides of the right triangle are corresponding sides of the three similar polygons. If the lengths of the three sides of the triangle, arranged in order of increasing magnitude, are a, b, c, and if the corresponding polygons are designated I, II, III, then, by Theorem 27, $\dfrac{I}{II} = \dfrac{a^2}{b^2}$ and $\dfrac{I}{III} = \dfrac{a^2}{c^2}$. This means that if area I is equal to $m \cdot a^2$, then area II is $m \cdot b^2$, and area III is $m \cdot c^2$. But $a^2 + b^2 = c^2$, by Principle 12. It follows that $ma^2 + mb^2 = mc^2$ and that I + II = III.

4. An edge of the new cube must be $\sqrt[3]{2}$ times the edge of the given cube.

5. The area of the new cube must be $\sqrt[3]{4}$ times the area of the given cube.

6. The ratio of the volumes of the two sizes of cup is 64:125. So two 5-cent cups are the better buy.

7. The old area is to the new area as 1600 is to 3025. So the increase in the amount of sheet iron is $\dfrac{1425}{1600}$ of the old amount, or 89.1%.

The old volume is to the new volume as 64,000 is to 166,375. So

- 119 -

the increase in capacity is $\frac{102,375}{64,000}$ of the old capacity, or just a trifle under 160%.

8. The sum of the squares on the other two sides of the right triangle is equal to the outside square minus two rectangles; and these two rectangles are equal to four right triangles.

9. The square on the hypotenuse is equal to the inner tilted square plus four right triangles. The sum of the squares on the other two sides is equal also to the inner tilted square plus four right triangles.

Page 209, line 3: "without defining it precisely." Every book on demonstrative geometry is obliged to define "circumference" at this point. Nothing we can say by way of definition, however, will carry more conviction than the pupil's well-established intuition on this subject, which in his mind is probably linked with the idea of "wrapping a string around the circle, unwinding, and holding it taut alongside a scale." Consequently we do well to get past the necessary definition of circumference as quickly and painlessly as possible, taking care, however, to make the definition not only simple, but accurate as well.

Page 209, line 8: Circumference as upper limit. The perimeter of an inscribed polygon of n sides obviously increases as n increases. It is obvious also that the perimeter of every inscribed polygon is less than the perimeter of every circumscribed polygon. Corollary 12c, page 94, is the authority for each of these obvious statements. So as n increases indefinitely the perimeter of an inscribed polygon of n sides must have an upper limit; for a variable that always increases while remaining less than a certain number (in this case the perimeter of some circumscribed polygon) cannot increase without limit.

Page 210, line 11: Area of circle as upper limit. The argument in this case is similar to that just given for the circumference. The obvious statements concerning area are supported by Area Assumption 1b, page 199.

In the discussion on pages 210-212 we arrive at the area of a circle by considering inscribed regular polygons and by allowing the number of sides to increase indefinitely by successive doubling. In the note on pages 224-225, irregular polygons are admitted and the manner in which the number of sides varies is not restricted to successive doubling.

Page 212, line 9. The dots after the numbers 6.2832 and 3.1416 are meant to indicate that each of these numbers is a non-ending decimal. Unfortunately, however, they give the impression that each of these numbers is correct so far as printed and continues indefinitely beyond the last printed digit. This is not true. The numbers would be correctly given as 6.28318 . . . and 3.14159 . . . . The more common form 3.1416 ought to be printed without dots and ought to be recognized as the rounded form of the non-ending decimal 3.14159 . . . .

Page 212, lines 15-16. The error is 3.142857 - 3.141592, or 0.0012(6).

Pages 213-217: Exercises. Exs. 1-6 make considerable demands upon arithmetic. The answers given here below have been computed with proper regard for significant figures. The teacher will do well, however, to express in advance his willingness to accept approximate answers that are less accurate than those here given.

There is virtue in carrying through occasional computations of considerable length. On the other hand there is danger that for some pupils protracted computations will obscure the main mathematical pattern. The ideal is that the pupil should be able to carry out a protracted computation and at the same time keep the main pattern clearly in mind. The teacher must judge how close to this ideal he can fairly expect his pupils to come.

1. 45.5 in.; 58.6(4) feet or 58 ft., 8 in.; 22 cm.

2. 165 sq. in.; 274 sq. ft.; 38.5 sq. cm.

3. 1.138 in.; 14.4 cm.

4. 2.489 ft.; 9.46 cm.

5. 18.4 sq. ft.; 58 sq. in.; $\frac{c^2}{4\pi}$ sq. in.

6. $c = 2\sqrt{\pi}\,\sqrt{A} = 3.54\sqrt{A}$.   87.1 cm.; 15.4 ft.; 32 in.

7. The two central angles in the triangles in Fig. 23 are equal, by
   Principle 8. Therefore each of the corresponding arcs is the same
   fractional part of its circumference. Since the circumferences have
   the same ratio as their radii, the arcs do also.

8. $\dfrac{A_1}{A_2} = \dfrac{r_1^2}{r_2^2} = \dfrac{c_1^2}{c_2^2}$

9. 4

10. 50 sq. in.

11. $2\frac{1}{4}$

12. $\dfrac{3}{2\sqrt{2}}$ or $\frac{3}{4}\sqrt{2}$

13. $\dfrac{15^2}{16^2}$ x 20 = 17.6 sq. in.

14. 4

15. $\sqrt{5}$, or 2.236

16. $4r^2 - \pi r^2 = \frac{6}{7} r^2$; $\pi r^2 - 2r^2 = \frac{8}{7} r^2$.

17. $\left(\dfrac{22}{7} \times 3 \times 7\right) + 2\left(\dfrac{22}{7} \cdot \dfrac{9}{4}\right) = 80\frac{1}{7}$ sq. in.

18. 7.6 inches

19. 4π

20. $\frac{4}{3}\pi$

21. $\dfrac{64}{3}\pi + 32\sqrt{3}$

22. Since $c^2 = a^2 + b^2$, $\dfrac{\pi}{2} \cdot \dfrac{c^2}{4} = \dfrac{\pi}{2} \cdot \dfrac{a^2}{4} + \dfrac{\pi}{2} \cdot \dfrac{b^2}{4}$. That is, the area of
   the largest semicircle is equal to the sum of the areas of the other
   two semicircles.

   Both the area of the triangle and the sum of the areas of the two
   shaded figures are equal to the area of the largest semicircle minus

the areas of two circular segments. (The term "circular segment" is not used in the text but will be clear to teachers at this point.)

Professor Norman Anning of the University of Michigan suggests that it is pertinent for teachers to point out that the Greeks, in their search for a means of computing the area of a circle, believed they were on the way to success when they could compute the area of a figure bounded entirely by arcs of circles. We now know that success was not to be attained in this way.

23. On page 211, $p_8 = 6.1232 \times 12$. Therefore $s_8 = 9.18$.

24. On page 211, $s_{2n} = \sqrt{2r^2 - r\sqrt{4r^2 - (s_n)^2}}$. When $n = 6$ we have $s_{12} = \sqrt{2r^2 - r^2\sqrt{3}} = r\sqrt{2 - \sqrt{3}} = .518r$. Therefore $p_{12} = 6.216r$, which falls short of the circumference by a little less than $0.07r$.

25. Perimeter $= 14 \times 5 \sin\left(\dfrac{360^\circ}{14}\right) = 70 \sin 25.7^\circ = 30.36$

26. The radius of the silo is about 8.3 feet. The sine of half the angle at the vertex is approximately $\dfrac{8.3}{11.2}$, or 0.741. Therefore the angle at the vertex is about 96°.

27. The term "lateral area" is probably new to the pupil, but clear enough from the context. The pupil has merely to add the areas of all the lateral faces of the prism. The theorem is not true unless all the lateral faces of the prism are perpendicular to each base; that is, unless the prism is a right prism. The bases need not be regular polygons.

28. The pupil can think of the cylindrical surface as slit parallel to the axis, unfolded, and laid out flat. The bases of the cylinder need not be circles, but the axis of the cylinder must be perpendicular to each base.

29. The term "slant height" should be clear from the formula and Fig. 30.

30. If the pupil will think of the conical surface as slit along an "element" of the cone, unfolded, and laid out flat, he will see that

he is asked to find the area of a sector of a circle of radius l and
of arc length c. The formula for the area of a sector, $\frac{1}{2}rs$, given
on page 213, becomes in this case $\frac{1}{2}lc$, or πrl.

Another way of regarding the lateral area of the cone is as the
limit of the lateral area of circumscribed regular pyramids as the
number of faces is indefinitely increased. That is, the limit of
$\frac{1}{2}pl$ is $\frac{1}{2}cl$, or πrl.

31. Extend one of the sides of the given polygon to form an exterior
    angle. Reproduce this angle at the center of the given circle, thus
    determining two vertices of the new polygon.

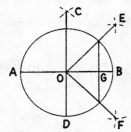 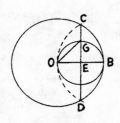

Fig. A

32. (See note following Ex. 36) If the radius of the given circle is r,
    the radius of the inner circle will be $\frac{r}{\sqrt{2}}$. This length is OG in
    each of the suggested constructions shown in Fig. A, in which all
    the points except O are determined in alphabetical order.

33. Determine r_1 and r_2 so that $r_1 : r_2 : r = 1 : \sqrt{2} : \sqrt{3}$. That is, $r_1 = \frac{r}{\sqrt{3}}$
    and $r_2 = \sqrt{2}\, r_1 = \frac{\sqrt{2}}{\sqrt{3}} r$. Fig. B, in which the points are determined
    in alphabetical order, shows one way of
    constructing AG equal to $\frac{r}{\sqrt{3}}$. AG times $\sqrt{2}$
    will give r_2.

34. Since $r_1 : r_2 : r_3 : \ldots : r = 1 : \sqrt{2} : \sqrt{3} : \ldots : \sqrt{n}$,
    the radius r_k of the kth inner circle is
    given by the equation $r_k = \frac{\sqrt{k}}{\sqrt{n}} \cdot r$.

35. Multiply any side of the given polygon by $\sqrt{n}$

Fig. B

to get the corresponding side
of the desired polygon.

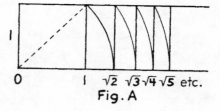

Fig. A

36. Multiply the radius of the
given circle by $\sqrt{\dfrac{m}{n}}$.

    Note: Exercises 32-36 can be
solved also by means of the
diagram at the right.

37. Their volumes have the ratio 1 to 8.

38. Their radii have the ratio 1 to $\sqrt[3]{2}$.

39. Since $r_1:r_2:r_3$. . .:$r = 1: \sqrt[3]{2} : \sqrt[3]{3} :. . . .: \sqrt[3]{n}$, the radius r_k of the

k^{th} inner sphere is given by the equation $r_k = \dfrac{\sqrt[3]{k}}{\sqrt[3]{n}} \cdot r$.

The teacher can add other questions similar to Exs. 37 and 38, such
as the following:

    If a watermelon 15 inches long can be bought for 40 cents, about
what should you expect to pay for a watermelon 20 inches long? Ans. 95¢

    If a salmon 35 inches long weighs 19 pounds, about how much will a
25-inch salmon weigh? Ans. 7 pounds

    If a boat 30 feet long weighs 3 tons, about how much will a similar
boat weigh that is 35 feet long? Ans. 4.8 tons

    Page 219, lines 5-7. The friction between the water and the pipe
will be least when, for a given cross-section of area, the perimeter is
as small as possible.

    Page 219, lines 8-9. Pinching the outer end of the exhaust pipe re-
duces the area of cross-section of the pipe. This increases the veloci-
ty of the exhaust gases, interfering with the vibration in such a way as
to reduce the noise of the exhaust. (It is not expected that pupils will
be able to answer this question from their knowledge of geometry alone.
It is expected that they will ask someone who knows something about
automobile engines.)

- 125 -

Page 219, lines 12-14. Since the spherical one has less surface it will be less exposed to the dissolving effect of the saliva.

Page 219, line 17. Professor Norman Anning of the University of Michigan points out that the phrase "any polyhedron" ought to be qualified to read "any polyhedron that you are likely to think of." There exist polyhedra, with holes, for which Euler's formula is not true.

Page 220, lines 1-3. Four? Yes, the regular octahedron. Five? Yes, the regular icosahedron. See Page 189. Six? No; for if so, then six faces would have a common vertex with six 60° angles at that point and the corner would be flattened down until the vertex ceased to exist.

Page 220, lines 4-6. Three regular pentagons? Yes, the regular dodecahedron, page 196. More than three? No. Three regular hexagons? No.

Page 220, lines 7-10. The five convex regular polyhedra are:

1. The _regular_ _tetrahedron_, four faces, in which three equilateral triangles meet at each vertex. See page 188.

2. The _cube_, six faces, in which three squares meet at each vertex.

3. The _regular_ _octahedron_, eight faces, in which four equilateral triangles meet at each vertex.

4. The _regular_ _dodecahedron_, twelve faces, in which three regular pentagons meet at each vertex.

5. The _regular_ _icosahedron_, twenty faces, in which five equilateral triangles meet at each vertex.

Page 221: Review Exercises.

1. Through each midpoint draw a line parallel to the line through the other two midpoints.

2. In triangles BCD and CBE (Fig. A) two angles of one are equal respectively to two angles of the other. Therefore these triangles, having BC in common, are equal, and CD = BE. Since ED

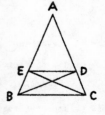

Fig. A

- 126 -

divides AB and AC proportionally, it is parallel to BC. (By Ex. 21 on
page 115, or directly by means of Principle 5, Case 1 of Similarity.)

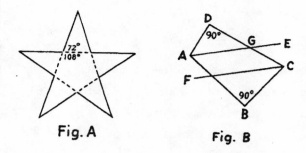

Fig. A   Fig. B

3. Make a regular five-pointed star by extending the sides of a regular
   pentagon, as shown in Fig. A. Each angle of the pentagon is 108°;
   each interior angle is 72°; the angle at each point of the star is 36°.

4. Since in Fig. B ∠B = ∠D = 90°, ∠A + ∠C = 180°, and ∠A must be
   less than 180°. Consequently AE, the bisector of angle A, must meet
   side DC at a point G which will be between D and C, or at C, or beyond
   C. In any case, ∠AGD = 90° - ½A by Principle 9. But ∠BCF = 90° -
   ½A also, since ∠A + ∠C = 180°. Therefore the bisectors AE and CF
   meet DC at the same angle and so are either parallel or coincident,
   by Theorem 14.

5. In Fig. C let H be the mid-point of AD.
   Then HM is parallel to DC, and consequently also to AB. Similarly HN, not
   assumed to contain the point M, is parallel to AB, and consequently also to

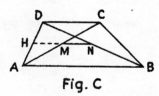

Fig. C

   DC. Therefore HM and HN must coincide (by Theorem 13), and MN is
   parallel to AB and CD.

6. Following the sort of argument used in Ex. 4 on page 127, let the
   line joining the mid-points M and N in Fig. A on the next page meet

AD extended at P and meet BC extended at Q.

Then $\frac{PM}{PN} = \frac{AM}{DN} = \frac{MB}{NC} = \frac{QM}{QN}$,

$\frac{PM}{PN} - 1 = \frac{QM}{QN} - 1,$

$\frac{NM}{PN} = \frac{NM}{QN}$, and PN = QN.

Therefore P and Q must coincide at the point

R which is common to AD extended and BC extended.

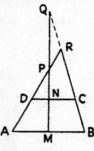

Fig. A

7. In Fig. B let the line joining the midpoints
of M and N meet AC at P and meet BD at Q.

Then $\frac{PM}{PN} = \frac{AM}{CN} = \frac{BM}{DN} = \frac{QM}{QN}$,

$\frac{PM}{PN} + 1 = \frac{QM}{QN} + 1,$

$\frac{MN}{PN} = \frac{MN}{QN}$, and PN = QN.

Therefore P and Q must coincide

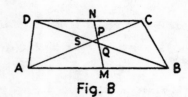

Fig. B

at point S which is common to both AC and BD.

First alternative proof:

Make the proof depend on Ex. 4, page 127, which states that if
three lines cut off proportional segments on two parallel lines, they
are either parallel or concurrent. In this case two of the three
lines are diagonals of the trapezoid and hence must intersect. Consequently all three lines AC, BD, and MN, must intersect.

Second alternative proof:

In Fig. C the diagonals AC and BD
intersect at O. Lines OM and ON
join O to the midpoints of AB and
CD. We must prove that MON is a
straight line.

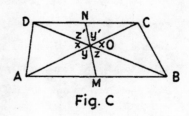

Fig. C

By Theorem 15 and Case 2 of Similarity, triangle OAB is similar to
triangle OCD. Therefore OC = k.OA; CD = k.AB; and CN = k.AM. By

Case 1 of Similarity, triangles OAM and OCN are similar and triangles OMB and OND are similar. Consequently $\angle y = \angle y'$, $\angle z = \angle z'$; $\angle x + \angle y + \angle z' = \angle x + \angle y' + \angle z = 180°$; and MON is a straight line.

8. The line joining the midpoints of the bases of a trapezoid passes through the point of intersection of the diagonals and through the point of intersection of the non-parallel sides extended. See Fig. A.

9. In Fig. B, arc AB = arc CD (by Theorem 19) and arc AC = arc BD (by Ex. 3, page 141). Therefore arc AB + arc AC = arc CD + arc BD = 180°.

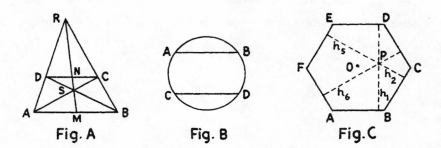

Fig. A   Fig. B   Fig. C

10. From any point P within the regular polygon draw lines to the vertices A, B, C, . . . and draw perpendiculars to the sides, extending the sides if necessary. Let the lengths of these perpendiculars from P to AB, BC, CD, ... be called h_1, h_2, h_3, ... respectively. Let the length of each side be <u>s</u>. Then the area of the polygon is equal to $\frac{s}{2}(h_1 + h_2 + h_3 + . . .)$. But the area of the polygon is also equal to half the perimeter times the apothem, a; that is, the area is equal to ½nsa. It follows that $(h_1 + h_2 + h_3 + . . .) = na$.

<u>Page 223, line 1</u>: "It can be proved." The proof is set forth in Killing and Hovestadt, <u>Handbuch des Mathematischen Unterrichts</u>, Vol. I, Teubner, Leipzig, 1910, pages 339-344.

<u>Page 223, line 12</u>: "as <u>n</u> increases indefinitely." Here we are no

longer constrained to allow $\underline{n}$ to increase by doubling, as on pages 210-212, but may allow $\underline{n}$ to increase at will through integral values.

Page 224, lines 13-14: "as the number of sides is increased indefi-nitely." Here also $\underline{n}$ is freed of the restriction to increase by dou-bling, and may increase at will through integral values.

Page 226, Fig. 43. The squares with solid lines for borders are the original squares of the grid. The squares with partially dotted borders are the result of halving the sides of each original square. Fig. 43 shows that, for the region depicted, this halving causes the difference between the two approximations to shrink from 4 square units to 8 quarter square units.

C H A P T E R   8

Euclid was obliged to recognize the existence of lengths which could not be represented by rational numbers. He had, moreover, no other numbers by which to represent these lengths. For example, the Pythagorean Theorem required that Euclid recognize the length of the diagonal of a rectangle whose length and width were 2 units and 1 unit respectively, even though he had no number by which to express this length. The best he could do was to "close in" upon this length by means of pairs of rational numbers, one member of the pair having its square less than 5 and the other having its square greater than 5. He could apprehend lengths of this sort only by means of inequalities, indefinitely many inequalities.

Consequently, when Euclid came to the point where he had to frame a definition of proportion, he was obliged to state it in such a way that some of the terms of the proportion could be "inexpressible" numbers like the length of this diagonal. This forced him to define proportion by means of equalities and inequalities, indefinitely many of each. That is why his Elements had to demonstrate many theorems concerning inequalities, a few of which still remain in our modern books on geometry, partly because of their traditional importance and partly because they are useful in other ways.

Euclid's definition of proportion, usually attributed to Eudoxus, is substantially as follows. Four quantities, a, b, c, d, are said to be in proportion - that is, $\frac{a}{b} = \frac{c}{d}$ - if equal multiples of a and c are both less than other equal multiples of b and d; or if not less than, then both equal to, or both greater than. Stated algebraically, if every

- 131 -

choice of integers m and n that makes ma $<$ nb also makes mc $<$ nd; if every choice of m and n that makes ma $=$ nb also makes mc $=$ nd; and if every choice of m and n that makes ma $>$ nb also makes mc $>$ nd, then we can write $\frac{a}{b} = \frac{c}{d}$ and can say that a, b, c, d are in proportion.

This is an overwhelming array of words and much more complicated than our modern definition of proportion, which is merely the expressed equality of two equal ratios. But in our modern definition we permit the numbers in our ratios to be irrational as well as rational, without expecting our pupils to have at hand an adequate definition of irrational numbers. In fact, when we come to grips with the matter we find that we ourselves must accept as definition of every irrational number a state-ment that involves inequalities in the same way as Euclid's (and Eudoxus') definition of proportion.

Euclid, lacking irrational numbers, had to face the difficulty occa-sioned by this lack when he was defining proportion. We have simplified the treatment of proportion by transferring the difficulty, together with Euclid's way of meeting it, to the definition of irrational numbers.

(See the notes on page 133 of this manual concerning page 229 of BASIC GEOMETRY.)

By taking the real number system, which consists of all the rational numbers and all the irrational numbers, as one of the bases of our geom-etry, we may ignore the traditional place of inequalities in geometry and may reserve only so much mention of them as other considerations seem to require. The first assumption of BASIC GEOMETRY, Principle 1, adopts the system of real numbers. So, from the very beginning, BASIC GEOMETRY applies alike to commensurable and incommensurable cases with-out requiring that these two sorts of cases be distinguished; and any mention we may wish eventually to make of inequalities may be withheld as long as we please.

- 132 -

In Chapter 8 we do not confine the discussion to inequalities; we show also the relation between geometric continuity and the continuity of the real number system. That is why this chapter is entitled "Continuous Variation."

Page 229, lines 15-16: "It can be proved. . ." For suppose that two integers p and q exist such that $\frac{p^2}{q^2} = 5$, where p and q have no common factor other than 1. Then one of the following three alternatives must be true: p alone contains 5 as a factor; q alone contains 5 as a factor; neither p nor q contains 5 as a factor. But each of these three alternatives contradicts the relation $p^2 = 5q^2$. Therefore no one of the three is possible, and there is no rational number whose square is 5.

Page 229, last two lines. The definition of $\sqrt{5}$ as a separation of the rational numbers reads substantially as follows: If the entire class of rational numbers be separated into two sub-classes such that every rational number is in one of these two sub-classes, and such that every positive rational number whose square is less than 5 is in one sub-class, together with zero and all the negative rationals, and every positive rational number whose square is not less than 5 is in the other sub-class, this very separation of the entire class of rationals in this manner defines a new number, not a rational, whose square is 5. We call it the positive square root of 5 and write it $\sqrt{5}$.

Page 231: Continuous variation of an angle. The continuous variation of angles ABX and XAB in Fig. 4 is obvious. The continuous variation of angle BXA follows from the fact that $\angle$ BXA = 180° - ($\angle$ ABX + $\angle$ XAB). As X varies continuously from C to D, $\angle$ BXA may have a numerical value that lies outside the range of values from $\angle$ BCA to $\angle$ BDA. It is necessary only that it begin with the numerical value of $\angle$ BCA and end with the numerical value of $\angle$ BDA, varying continuously in some way from one to the other.

- 133 -

If the curve along which X varies happens to be a circular arc that passes through A and B, the size of angle BXA does not change, and the sum of angles ABX and XAB is constant. Nevertheless we may still speak of the continuous variation of angle BXA. For the mathematician regards both $y = ax$ and $y = c$ as examples of the continuous variation of y. It is not lack of variability in the colloquial sense that we must guard against, but lack of continuity.

Page 232, lines 13-14: "q varies continuously toward $0°$," perhaps merely decreasing from its initial value, perhaps first increasing and then decreasing.

Page 232, Theorem 29. If a is not greater than b, then either $a = b$ or $a < b$. But each of these alternatives has a consequence that contradicts the given relation $\angle p > \angle q$. Therefore the assumption that a is not greater than b is false.

Page 233, line 20: "Why?" If $b' = b$, then $\angle q' = \angle q$, by Principle 8. But this contradicts the given relation $\angle q > \angle q'$.

Page 233: Theorem 31. If $\angle q$ is not greater than $\angle q'$, then either $\angle q = \angle q'$ or $\angle q < \angle q'$. But each of these alternatives has a consequence that contradicts the given relation $b > b'$. Therefore the assumption that $\angle q$ is not greater than $\angle q'$ is false.

Page 234: Exercises.

1. The central angles corresponding to the two minor arcs are unequal. Apply Theorem 30.

2. Apply Theorem 31 and consider the minor arcs that correspond to the two angles of the triangles at the center of the circle.

3. In Fig. 10, $AB < BC$. Therefore $\frac{1}{2}AB < \frac{1}{2}BC$; that is, $MB < BN$. It follows from Theorem 28 that $\angle p > \angle q$. Consequently $\angle y > \angle x$ and $MO > NO$.

4. In Fig. 10, $MO > NO$. Therefore $\angle y > \angle x$, $\angle p > \angle q$, $BN > MB$, and $AB < BC$.

5. See Fig. A at the top of the next page.

- 134 -

5. a + b > x

   c + d > x

   a + d > y

   b + c > y

   —————————————

   2a + 2b + 2c + 2d > 2x + 2y

   a + b + c + d > x + y

Fig. A

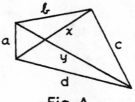

Fig. B

Page 235, lines 10-12. In Chapter 2, page 49, we made no use of directed angles there described. It would have been impossible at that time to have considered the sum of the angles of a "cross polygon" of the sort shown here in Fig. B. Indeed, in the case of such polygons, it is not easy to decide which angle at each vertex shall be called the interior angle of the polygon. The student can show that the sum of the counter-clockwise angles at the vertices of any polygon, whether convex or cross, is $(n - 2)180° \pm k \quad 360°$, where k is either zero or some positive or negative integer. An exercise of this sort shows the increased generalization that is possible under the concept of directed angles.

Pages 236-240: Exercises. Most of these exercises require merely that the pupil verify by his own thinking the results already set down in the book in the form of statements, or illustrated by Fig. 13 on page 239 of BASIC GEOMETRY.

1. More exaggerated forms of Fig. 13a and Fig. 13h will show this.

2. In answering this question the pupil anticipates by his own efforts the series of diagrams shown in Fig. 13.

3. The directed angle $x_+ = \frac{1}{2}(\angle BOD_+ - \angle COA_+) = \frac{1}{2}(\angle BOD_+ + \angle AOC_-) = \frac{1}{2}(\widehat{BD}_+ + \widehat{AC}_-)$, where $\widehat{BD}_+$ is used to represent the measure of the directed central angle corresponding to the directed arc $\widehat{BD}_+$.

4. The directed angle $x_+ = \frac{1}{2}(\angle BOD_+) = \frac{1}{2}(\widehat{BD}_+)$. Since C coincides with A,

$\angle COA = \angle AOC = 0^{\circ}$. Consequently $\widehat{AC}$, intentionally printed without a subscript sign because $\widehat{AC}$ is zero, may be inserted in the parenthesis in order to preserve the form of the algebra. See page 236, lines 21-23.

8. The pupil must see that $360^{\circ} - \widehat{DA}_+$ can be replaced by $\widehat{AD}_+$.

10. The directed angle $x_+ = \frac{1}{2}(360^{\circ}) - y_+ = \frac{1}{2}(360^{\circ} - \widehat{CA}_+ + \widehat{BD}_+) = \frac{1}{2}(\widehat{AC}_+ + \widehat{BD}_+)$.

11. In circle i, $\frac{1}{2}(\widehat{BD}_+ + \widehat{AC}_+) = \frac{1}{2}(360^{\circ})$.

   In circle j, $\angle x_+ = 180^{\circ} + \frac{1}{2}(\widehat{BD}_+ + \widehat{AC}_-)$, from Ex. 3. But $360^{\circ} + \widehat{AC}_- = \widehat{AC}_+$. Therefore $x_+ = \frac{1}{2}(\widehat{BD}_+ + \widehat{AC}_+)$.

   In circle k, $\widehat{AC}_+$ represents the measure of the central angle corresponding to the complete circumference, directed positively.

12. $\overline{PA}$ is positive, decreasing toward zero; $\overline{PB}$ is positive, approaching $\overline{AB}$; $\overline{PA} \times \overline{PB}$ is positive, decreasing toward zero.

13. Zero

14. $\overline{PA}$ is negative, decreasing algebraically toward $\overline{BA}$; $\overline{PB}$ is positive, decreasing toward zero; $\overline{PA} \times \overline{PB}$ is zero when P is at A, negative when P is between A and B; zero again when P is at B.

15. Zero

16. $\overline{PA}$ and $\overline{PB}$ are both negative and decreasing algebraically; $\overline{PA} \times \overline{PB}$ is positive and increasing.

17. Covered by answers to Exs. 12-16.

18. The perimeters of the rectangles in Fig. 14 are all equal; so the square has the largest area and the product rs is greatest when r = s.

   By the second suggested method, $\overline{AP} \times \overline{PB} = \left(\frac{\overline{AB}}{2} - \overline{PM} \right) \times \left(\frac{\overline{AB}}{2} + \overline{PM} \right) = \frac{(\overline{AB})^2}{4} - (\overline{PM})^2$. This has its greatest value, namely $\frac{(\overline{AB})^2}{4}$, when $\overline{PM} = 0$. Therefore the largest negative value attained by $\overline{PA} \times \overline{PB}$ is $- \frac{(\overline{AB})^2}{4}$. This occurs when P is at M, midway between A and B.

CHAPTER 9

Lesson Plan Outline: 14 lessons

1-6. Through page 253

7-13. Exercises, pages 254-261

14. Pages 261-266

Page 241. The two 9:14 p.m. lines on the chart ought, strictly, to be arcs of great circles.

Page 243, line 16. The locus is a circular cylinder of radius 2 in.

Page 244, line 1. The locus is composed of four straight line segments, each equal in length to a side of the square, and four quadrants of a circle whose radius is equal to the radius of the rolling circle.

Page 244, line 3. An example of a locus that consists of only one point is the locus of all points in a plane that are equidistant from three given points in the plane. An example of a locus that consists of a curve and a single isolated point is the locus of all points in a plane at a distance r from a circle of radius r that lies in the plane.

Pages 244-246: Exercises.

1. A circle, center at 0, radius 5 inches.

2. Two parallel lines, each 4 inches from the given line. When the fixed line is perpendicular to the plane, the locus is a circle of radius 4 inches.

3. The four points in which the circle with center 0 and radius 5 inches intersects the two lines that are parallel to AB and 4 inches from AB. These four points are the corners of a rectangle, 8 inches by 6 inches.

4. The three points common to the circle and to the two lines that are parallel to AB and 4 inches from it. One of these lines is tangent to the circle. These three points are the vertices of a triangle of base 8 inches and altitude 8 inches.

5. A straight line midway between the two given lines.

6. Two lines parallel to the given lines, one on each side of the plane of the given lines and distant $\sqrt{5}$ inches from this plane.

7. Two lines, each parallel to the base of the triangle and at a distance equal to the altitude.

8. A line perpendicular to the chord and midway between one extremity of the chord and its perpendicular bisector.

9. Two lines, each making an angle of $30°$ with the given line.

10. A straight line perpendicular to the diameter (extended) through P. This straight line meets the diameter extended at a point D such that $OD \cdot OP = r^2$, where O is the center of the circle and r its radius. All that is expected of the pupil is that he shall plot enough points of the locus to surmise that it is a straight line. As P approaches O, the locus recedes from O; when P is at O, the locus has vanished.

The proof, which is not expected of the pupil, will be of interest to the teacher. The similar right triangles OAD and OPA in Fig. A tell us that $\frac{OD}{r} = \frac{r}{OP}$. Another pair of similar triangles tells us that $\frac{OT}{r} = \frac{r}{OM}$. Therefore $OD \times OP = OT \times OM$ and $\frac{OD}{OT} = \frac{OM}{OP}$. Since triangles ODT and OMP have angle MOP in common and the sides including this angle proportional, the two triangles are similar. Consequently angle ODT is equal to angle OMP, which is $90°$.

Fig. A

This locus can be thought of as the inverse of the circle on OP as diameter, using the given circle as circle of inversion. See pages 263-264. So considered it involves the converse of the theorem on page 264, lines 17-27, namely Ex. 2 on page 265.

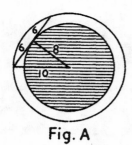

Fig. A

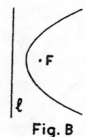

Fig. B

11. If one side of the square is s, the locus is a quadrant of a circle of radius s, a quadrant of a circle of radius s√2, and another quadrant of a circle of radius s.

12. A circle concentric with the given circle and of radius 8. See Fig. A.

13. A parabola. Of course, the pupil is not expected to know anything about the curve he has plotted, not even its name. The teacher can tell him. See Fig. B.

14. Both branches of a hyperbola. Many students will draw only the right-hand branch. See Ex. 13 and Fig. C.

15. An ellipse, as shown in Fig. D.

16. Four straight line segments, each 1 inch long, and four quadrants of a circle of radius $\frac{3}{2}$ inches. In Fig. E, M is the mid-point of the hypotenuse of a right triangle; consequently M is at a distance $\frac{3}{2}$ inches from the vertex of the right angle.

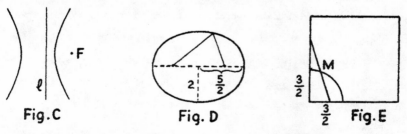

Fig. C   Fig. D   Fig. E

Page 246, fifth line from bottom. The wording "is a point of" is mathematically precise and is in harmony with the definition of locus on

- 139 -

page 242. The wording "point lies on curve," "lies on line," "lies in plane" is merely a mathematical colloquialism. We use it here because it is familiar.

Page 247. The student may need to look back at the discussion of Indirect Method on pages 33-35 of BASIC GEOMETRY. There is a comment on page 35 of this manual concerning pages 33-35 of BASIC GEOMETRY that is pertinent here.

Page 248: Locus Theorem 1. Actually on page 133 we do not define "circle" in the strictly precise locus terminology involving "all the points, and no other points" because it is too awkward to bring it in there. Instead, we do what amounts to the same thing by describing "all other points" as being inside or outside the circle.

Page 248: Fig. 5. To have put the point R on the line PQ would have been to beg the question, to assume what must be proved. Placing R on one side of line PQ seems to assume what can be proved to be false. In all such cases geometers prefer to lead pupils to reason correctly from incorrect figures than to lead pupils, by means of correct figures, to make premature and incorrect inferences.

Page 249, line 22. First "Why:" by Corollary 14a. Second "Why:" by Ex. 2 on page 113.

Page 250, lines 8-9. The locus is a plane perpendicular to the plane of the given parallel lines, parallel to them and midway between them.

Page 251, line 19. The locus is a plane perpendicular to the line segment joining the two given points and bisecting this line segment.

Page 252, lines 13-16. In each case the locus is a pair of planes which bisect the angles formed by the given lines or planes.

Pages 254-261: Exercises.

1. The perpendicular bisector of the base.

2. A straight line midway between the two given parallels.

3. A straight line parallel to the given line and midway between it and the given point.

4. Two parallel lines, one on each side of BC, both equally distant from it.

5. Two straight lines through A, each making an angle of 45° with AB. Most students will think of AB as horizontal and will construe "upper" literally. Let them suppose that AB is vertical.

6. A straight line perpendicular to XY at P.

7. A circle having the given point as center and the given radius as its radius.

8. The perpendicular bisector of the line segment joining the two points.

9. A circle concentric with the given circle. Its radius will be $\sqrt{r^2 - \frac{1^2}{4}}$, where r is the radius of the given circle and l is the length of the chords.

10. A straight line midway between the two fixed parallels. This is true whether the exercise is interpreted as meaning that each circle cuts a pair of equal chords, the pairs themselves being unequal, or whether the pairs also must be equal.

11. Both the center of the circle and the point of intersection of the two tangents are equidistant from the points of contact. Hence they must lie on the perpendicular bisector of the chord of contact.

12. Since each mid-point is equidistant from the ends of the chord, the two mid-points must lie on the perpendicular bisector of the chord.

13. The center and the mid-points of the arcs are all equidistant from the ends of the chord; consequently they must lie on the perpendicular bisector of the chord.

14. The center of each circle is equidistant from the ends of the common chord. Hence the two centers must lie on the perpendicular bisector of the common chord.

- 141 -

15. By Ex. 13, the center of the circle lies on the perpendicular bisector of each chord. But the perpendicular bisector of one chord must
be perpendicular to the other chord also, so the two perpendicular
bisectors must coincide.

16. The diameter perpendicular to any chord of the system, by Ex. 15.

17. Draw any two chords. Their perpendicular bisectors will meet at the
center.

18. The perpendicular bisectors of two sides AB and BC of any triangle
ABC cannot be parallel; for if they were, the two sides would be
parallel, or coincident. It follows that the two perpendicular bisectors must have a point in common. This point must be equidistant
from A and B, and equidistant also from B and C. Since it is equidistant from A and C, it must lie on the perpendicular bisector of
the third side, AC, also.

19. The bisectors of two angles A and B of any triangle ABC cannot be
parallel; for if they were, angles A and B would add up to 180°. It
follows that the two bisectors must have a point in common. This
point must be equidistant from AB and AC, and equidistant also from
BA and BC. Since it is equidistant from AC and BC, it must lie on
the bisector of the third angle C, also.

20. In contrast with the construction on page 181 of BASIC GEOMETRY, the
emphasis in this exercise is now on the phrase "and only one." The
proof follows immediately from Ex. 18 in this set of exercises.

21. Ordinarily the point of intersection of the first and second perpendicular bisectors will not coincide with the point of intersection
of the second and third perpendicular bisectors.

22. A segment of the bisector of each angle of the triangle, each segment
extending from vertex to incenter. See Ex. 19.

23. A pair of lines parallel to the given lines. If the distances from

the given lines l and m respectively are in the ratio p to q, one of the new lines will be at the distance $\left(\dfrac{p}{p + q}\right)$ d from l and the other will be at the distance $\left(\dfrac{p}{q - p}\right)$ d from l, where d is the distance between l and m. The second part of this answer can be got by solving the equation $\dfrac{y}{y + d} = \dfrac{p}{q}$.

24. With P as center draw a circle that will cut the given circle in two points A and B. Draw the perpendicular bisector of AB. Finally, draw at P the perpendicular to this perpendicular bisector.

25. A circle concentric with the given circle and having a radius equal to $\sqrt{r^2 + t^2}$.

26. An arc of the circle that has for its diameter the line segment joining the center and the given external point. Every point of this arc is inside the given circle.

27. The circle that has for its diameter the line segment joining the center O of the concentric circles and the given external point P. Points O and P do not belong to the locus.

28. A circle concentric with the given circle and having a radius of 10 feet.

29. Two equal circles, each having half the base for its diameter. The mid-point of the base does not belong to the locus.

30. Same locus as in Ex. 29, except that now the end-points of the base are also excluded from the locus.

31. A circle having for diameter the line segment joining the given point and the center of the given circle. The given point does not belong to the locus.

32. Same locus as in Ex. 31, except that now the given point is included in the locus.

33. A circle with center at the intersection of the two fixed rods and with radius equal to $\dfrac{1}{2}$, where l is the length of the moving rod.

The mid-point M of the moving rod is always the mid-point of the hypotenuse of a right triangle and so is always the same distance, $\frac{1}{2}$, from the ends of the moving rod and from the point of intersection of the two fixed rods.

34. Assume that the theorem is not true. It is still possible to pass a circle through three vertices of the given quadrilateral; the fourth vertex will be either inside or outside the circle. The two angles that are given as having the sum 180° must be equal to two central angles that add up to 360°. But under the assumption that the fourth vertex is not on the circle, the two given supplementary angles are equal to two central angles that add up to something more or less than 360°· a contradiction. Therefore the fourth vertex must be on the circle.

35. A circle having AB as chord. Its center Q will be outside the given circle, on the perpendicular bisector of AB, and such that angle AQB is equal to 180° minus the central angle in the given circle corresponding to the minor arc AB. The proof depends on Locus Theorem 7 and Exs. 5 and 6, pages 147 and 148.

36. The phrase "segment of a circle" has not been defined previously; the description in parenthesis is sufficient to show its meaning.

If O is the center of the given circle, if P is the point of intersection of AC and BD, and if P' is the point of intersection of AD and BC, then angle APB is always 30° and angle AP'B is always 90°.

(a) The locus of P is an arc of a second circle having AB as chord and such that the minor arc AB of this second circle has a central angle of 60°. This means that the center Q of the second circle is "above" AB, on the perpendicular bisector of AB, and such that angle AQB is equal to 60°. Consequently Q is on the given circle, twice as far above O as O is above AB. The extent of the arc that constitutes the locus of P can be determined as follows.

One limiting position of CD makes C coincide with A. In this position ∠BAD = 90° and BD extended meets the second circle at A', so that ∠BAA' = 120° and A'Q is parallel to AB. The other limiting position of CD makes D coincide with B. In this position AC extended meets the second circle at B', so that ∠ABB' = 120° and QB' is parallel to AB. The straight line A'QB' is tangent to the given circle and is a diameter of the second circle. Except for the end-points A' and B', all points of the second circle "above" this diameter constitute the locus of P. That is, the locus is a semicircle minus its end-points.

(b) The locus of P' is an arc of a third circle having AB as chord and such that arc AB of this third circle has a central angle of 90°. This means that the center R of this third circle is the mid-point of AB, and the locus of P' is the "upper" semicircle of this third circle, including the end-points A and B.

37. Each of the given triangles has its vertex V on one of two equal arcs of the sort shown in Fig. 11, page 253, in connection with Locus Theorem 7. For all positions of V on one of these arcs the desired locus is the complete circle that contains the other arc, except for that point on the major arc AB that is equidistant from A and B. This excepted point is approached on each side by the point of intersection P of the perpendiculars as V approaches first A and then B. But this excepted point cannot belong to the locus because V cannot coincide with either A or B.

When ∠VAB = 90°, A is seen to belong to the locus. Similarly for B, when ∠VBA = 90°. When V is between these two positions, ∠APB is the supplement of the given angle. When V is outside these two positions, ∠APB is equal to the given angle.

The entire locus, then, is made up of the two equal circles containing the arcs to which vertex V is always restricted, except for the point on each circle that is farthest from AB.

38. The line segment joining the mid-point of the base to the opposite
vertex. This line is defined on page 259 as a _median_ of the triangle.

39. The center will be at the point where the bisector of the 114° angle
intersects a parallel to one of the given lines that is 100 feet
distant from this given line.

40. For every position of CD angle C is unaltered in size; similarly for
angle D. Consequently angle DBC must be constant also.

41. Drop AD perpendicular to MR and continue it to A' so that A'D = AD.
The intersection of A'B and MR is the desired point.

42. Same as Ex. 41.

43. In Fig. 21 on page 259 of BASIC GEOMETRY, quadrilateral ABCB' is a
parallelogram in which ∠B' = ∠B, AB' = BC, and AB = B'C. Similarly
for quadrilaterals BCAC' and CABA'. Consequently triangle A'B'C' is
similar to triangle ABC and sides A'B', B'C', and C'A' are bisected
by C, A, and B respectively. So the altitudes of the given triangle
are the perpendicular bisectors of the sides of the new triangle,
and hence (by Ex. 18, page 255) meet in a point.

44. The suggestion given in the exercise is enough.

45. The point of intersection of each pair of tangents is on a bisector
of an angle of the triangle formed by joining the centers of the
three circles. Since it must be on all three bisectors, it must be
the point that is common to all three bisectors (by Ex. 19, page 256).

46. The locus consists of two lines, which
can be constructed as follows. Draw
a line parallel to AB and two units
away from AB. Draw two lines at a
distance of one unit from AC, one on
each side of AC. These two lines
will intersect the first line at P

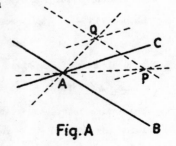

Fig. A

and Q, as in Fig. A. The lines AP and AQ, extended, constitute the locus.

It is easy to prove that every point on AP is twice as far from AB as from AC, and that every point on AQ is twice as far from AB as from AC. In each case one needs only two pairs of similar right triangles.

The difficulty in this exercise consists in proving the converse, namely: if $\frac{PB}{PC} = \frac{2}{1}$ and if $\frac{P'B'}{P'C'} = \frac{2}{1}$, then P' must lie on AP (extended). Angles BPC and B'P'C' are equal, since each is the supplement of angle A. Consequently triangles BPC and B'P'C' are similar, and $\angle$ PBC = $\angle$ P'B'C'. It follows that BC and B'C' are parallel, since each meets AB' at the same angle. Therefore $\frac{AB}{AB'} = \left(\frac{BC}{B'C'}\right) = \frac{BP}{B'P'}$; the right triangles ABP and AB'P' are similar; $\angle$ BAP = $\angle$ B'AP'; and P' lies on AP.

Fig. A

The proof for Q and Q' follows the pattern of the preceding proof for P and P' with only one change: angles BQC and B'Q'C' are now equal to angle A instead of to its supplement.

47. $\frac{AR}{RB} = \left(\frac{AP}{PB}\right) = \frac{QA}{QB} = \frac{m}{n}$. See note following Ex. 26 on page 116.

48. It is evident from the preceding exercise that R and Q are two points on the desired locus. Any other point P on the locus must be such that $\frac{AP}{PB} = \frac{m}{n} = \frac{AR}{RB} = \frac{QA}{QB}$. This means that $\angle$QPR must equal 90°, by Ex. 27, page 117. So the locus of P is the circle on QR as diameter.

49. We can think of the given parallel lines as being perpendicular to the plane of page 260, so that these lines - when viewed end-on - are represented by the points A and B of Fig. 23 on that page. From Ex. 48 on page 260 we know that the locus of points whose distances from A and B are in a given ratio is the circle that has QR for

diameter. So in this Ex. 49 the locus must be a cylinder with axis
through the midpoint of QR and perpendicular to the plane of page 260.
That is, the locus is a cylinder with axis parallel to the given
parallel lines.

50. The locus is a circle in the given plane with center D and radius 3.
For every point in the plane that is 5 inches from P must be 3 inches
from D.

51. The intersection is a circle with center at D, the foot of the perpendicular dropped to the plane from P, the center of the sphere.
See Fig. 24, page 261. For if the radius of the sphere is r, every
point of the intersection of plane and sphere will be at the same
distance, $\sqrt{r^2 - (PD)^2}$, from D.

52. Every point of the intersection of two spheres with centers O and O'
will lie in a plane perpendicular to OO'. See Ex. 14, page 143. So
the intersection of the two spheres can be regarded as the intersection of this plane and either one of the spheres. By the preceding
exercise this is a circle.

Page 261, line 16. See Ex. 37, page 151. In this connection Professor Norman Anning of the University of Michigan suggests that we write
$PA \cdot PB = (PT)^2 = (PO)^2 - r^2 = (PO + r)(PO - r)$ and show that this last
way of writing the product is valid even when P is inside the circle. It
is clear from Fig. 25 on page 261 that when P is inside the circle,
$PA' \cdot PB' = (PO + r)(PO - r)$ and the power is negative, as stated in the
text. It is interesting to add to this the note that when P is outside
the circle, the power of the point is equal to the square of the tangent
from P to the circle; and when P is inside the circle, the power of the
point is equal to minus the square of half the shortest chord through P.

Page 262: Exercises.

1. The proof follows immediately from the definition of power of a point

with respect to a circle on page 261. For every point P on the
common chord, and on the common chord extended, the product PA · PB
is the same for both circles.

2. This is a limiting case of the preceding exercise. If the circles
   are externally tangent at T, the power of any point P on the common
   internal tangent is $(PT)^2$ with respect to both circles.

3. If the circles are internally tangent at T, the power of any point P
   on the common external tangent is the same, namely $(PT)^2$, with respect to both circles.

Page 262, fourth line from bottom. The substitution of $(TP)^2$ for
$(T'P)^2$ is intentional. By suppressing this detail the subtraction of
the equation in this line from the equation in the line above is more
easily followed.

Page 263: Exercises.

1. The foregoing proof can be applied without alteration to the case of
   two intersecting circles. It follows from Ex. 1 on page 262 that
   each of the two points of intersection of the two circles has the
   same power with respect to both circles. Both of these points must
   lie on PD, therefore, and PD must be the common chord (extended).

2. Both in the case of two circles that are externally tangent and of
   two circles that are internally tangent, it seems reasonable and
   helpful to define the radical axis as the common tangent of the two
   circles.

3. A plane perpendicular to the line of centers of the two spheres. The
   student is not expected to be able to prove this. Actually the proof
   follows the same pattern as the proof in the case of two circles, on
   pages 262-263. Given a point P having the same power with respect
   to two spheres with centers at O and O'; Fig. 27 on page 262 can be
   considered as representing the section made by the plane POO', except

- 149 -

that points T and T' ordinarily will not be in this plane. But the relations $(PO)^2 = (OT)^2 + (TP)^2$ and $(PO')^2 = (O'T')^2 + (T'P)^2$ hold just as before.

Page 264, line 13. The inverse of the circle of inversion is the circle of inversion itself.

Page 264, line 16. The radius of a circle with center at O times the radius of the circle that is its inverse is equal to the square of the radius of the circle of inversion. The centers of all three circles are at the center of inversion, O.

Page 264, line 26: "Why?" Because triangles OQP and OP'Q' are similar by the Principle of Similarity, Case 1, and angle OP'Q' is given a right angle.

Pages 264-265: Exercises.

1. The foregoing proof applies in each case without alteration. When P' is on the circle of inversion it coincides with P, and the radius OP' of the circle of inversion is the diameter of the circle that is the inverse of the straight line through P'.

2. The inverse is a straight line perpendicular to the line of centers OO' of the two circles. In Fig. A, let OP be the diameter of the given circle that passes through O. If P' is the inverse of P, and Q' the inverse of a random point Q on the given circle, then $OP \cdot OP' = r^2 = OQ \cdot OQ'$ and $\dfrac{OP}{OQ} = \dfrac{OQ'}{OP'}$.
Therefore triangles POQ and Q'OP' are similar (Principle of Similarity, Case 1) and $\angle OQP = \angle OP'Q'$. But $\angle OQP = 90°$, being

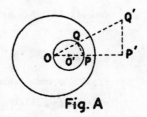

Fig. A

inscribed in a semicircle. Therefore Q'P' is perpendicular to OP' at P', when Q is any point of the given circle except O or P. So the locus of the inverses of all points of the given circle is the straight line through P' perpendicular to OP.

Page 265, lines 10-11. A line segment equal in length to the diameter of the circle.

Page 265, lines 12-15. A circle equal to the circular edge of the coin. Usually an ellipse; but when the two planes are perpendicular, the projection is a line segment equal in length to the diameter of the coin.

Page 265, lines 16-18. A circle. No.

CHAPTER 10

Lesson Plan Outline: 7 lessons

1-2. Pages 268-278

3-6. Exercises, pages 278-280

7. Pages 280-283

It is important for the teacher to note that Chapter 10 extends the ideas of Chapter 1, but that the pupil needs the background of the intervening chapters in order to appreciate this final chapter. This connection between Chapter 10 and all that precedes it is set forth on pages 268-269, 273, 277-278, 280, and 283.

One aim of this final chapter is to reconsider the logical structure of this geometry and to look more closely at the part played by certain basic principles and theorems of this geometry. Another aim is to consider the logical structure of other geometries; to consider then the structure of logical systems in general; and finally to recognize that this geometry affords an instructive example of a logical system and is a convenient and proper pattern for all logical thinking.

Page 268, line 18. The "ten statements" is correct here, because three of the thirteen exercises on pages 161-163 do not concern non-mathematical situations.

Pages 270-273: Exercises. As explained on page 269 the pupil is not expected to find "the correct answer" to these exercises.

Pages 274-276: Exercises.

1. No.

2. No. It might be an ellipsoid or other curved surface.

3. Keep it covered and chilled.

4. Cut a loaf into slices. Keep two slices dry and covered, but one warm and the other cold; keep two more slices moist and covered, but one warm and the other cold; keep two more dry and uncovered, but

one warm and the other cold; keep two more moist and uncovered, but
one warm and the other cold. Then observe which slice of each pair
becomes moldy sooner. Test four more pairs with respect to moist
and dry, and four more with respect to covered and uncovered.

5. Evidently it is not the air by itself that causes fermentation, but
   something in the air that is more commonly found in thickly settled
   regions than on mountain tops.

6. Heat the milk sufficiently to kill the ferment, or to kill most of
   it. Then chill the milk to discourage the growth of any of the ferment that remains alive. Also, keep air away from the milk.

7. The object is to drive out as much of the air as possible and then
   to kill the harmful bacteria that may be left inside the jars.

8. Because the pus-forming bacteria in the air were killed in passing
   through the carbolated gauze.

9. In the ice cream.   10. In the canned lobster.

Pages 278-280: Exercises.

1, 2, 3, 5, 6. In lines 17-19, on page 278, the student is reminded that
he skipped the proofs of Principles 6, 7, 8, 11 and perhaps of Theorem 13 also. These proofs are given in the book on the pages mentioned in these exercises.

4.   Given: Triangles ABC and
     A'B'C' (Fig. A) in which
     ∠A = ∠A', A'B' = k·AB,
     and A'C' = k·AC.

     To Prove: Triangle A'B'C'
similar to triangle ABC.

     Proof: At B' draw B'C" so

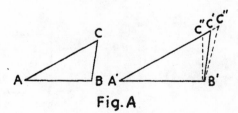

Fig. A

that ∠A'B'C" equals ∠B. This line will meet A'C' (extended beyond
the point C' if necessary) in the point C". By Case 2 of Similarity,

- 153 -

which for the moment is being taken as a fundamental postulate, triangles ABC and A'B'C" are similar and A'C" = k·AC. But A'C' = k·AC
(Given). Therefore A'C" = A'C' and C" must coincide with C'. It follows that ∠ A'B'C' = ∠ B and triangles ABC and A'B'C' are similar.

   Case 3 can now be proved, just as on pages 79-80 of BASIC GEOMETRY.

7. Most of the answer is given on page 106 of BASIC GEOMETRY. The answer there given and the form in which this Ex. 7 is worded both
imply that our chief interest here is in getting back to Principle 5.
Actually Principles 4 and 3 are also required in the proof of Theorem
13. Schematically the dependence of Theorem 13 upon these three
principles can be shown as follows.

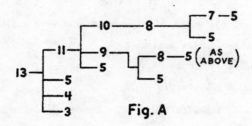

Fig. A

8. The dependence of Theorem 16 on Theorems 15, 14, and 13 and so back
   to Principle 5 is shown in the following diagram.

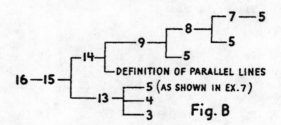

Fig. B

9. The dependence of Theorem 20 on earlier theorems is shown in the
   diagram on the next page (Fig. A).

10. On page 247 we have seen that if a proposition is true, its opposite
    converse is true also. So, instead of proving Theorem 21 directly

- 154 -

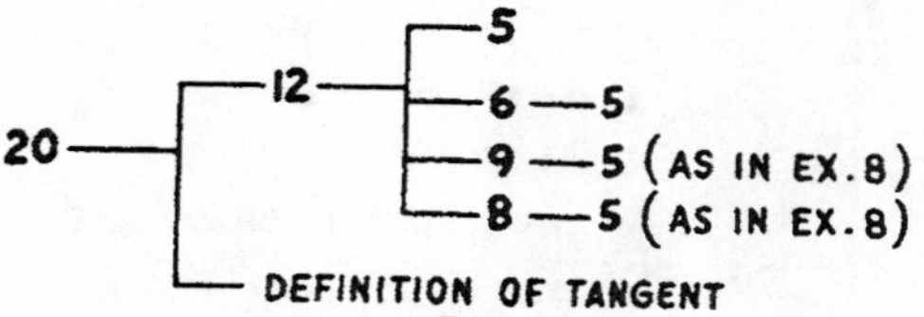

Fig. A

by showing that a given tangent is perpendicular to the radius, we
show instead that a line through T (page 139, Fig. 13) that is not
perpendicular to the radius OT cannot be tangent. This is as much
as is expected of the student.

The teacher will observe that the proof on page 140 of BASIC GEOME-
TRY proceeds on the tentative assumption that l, given tangent, is
not perpendicular to OT. Under this tentative assumption it considers the possibility that OU equals OT and then that OU is less than
OT. In each case it arrives at a contradiction. Consequently
the tentative assumption of non-perpendicularity is incompatible
with the given condition that l is tangent.

11. The proof of Theorem 22 depends upon earlier theorems as indicated
below.

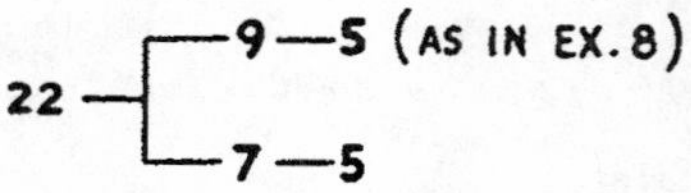

Fig. B

12. The dependence of Theorem 23 upon the fundamental principles of this
geometry is shown in the diagram on the next page (Fig. A).

13. Any parallelogram having one side equal to b and the altitude upon
this side equal to h can be divided into two triangles, each of side b
and altitude h, by drawing either one of the diagonals of the parallelogram. Consequently the area of the parallelogram is $2(\frac{1}{2}bh)$, or
bh. Every rectangle is a special sort of parallelogram and so its

- 155 -

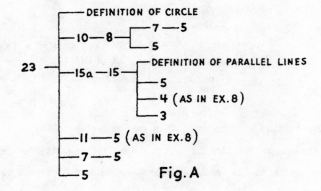

DEFINITION OF CIRCLE

23 ── 10 ── 8 ──┬── 7 ── 5
               └── 5

        15a ── 15 ──── DEFINITION OF PARALLEL LINES
                   ├── 5
                   ├── 4 (AS IN EX.8)
                   └── 3

        ── 11 ── 5 (AS IN EX.8)
        ── 7 ── 5
        ── 5

Fig. A

area is equal to bh also. The area of any polygon can now be found just as described on pages 203-204 of BASIC GEOMETRY.

The contrast in procedure here is between the order rectangle - right triangle - any triangle - parallelogram - polygon and the order triangle - parallelogram (rectangle) - polygon.

14. In Fig. 9, page 32, of BASIC GEOMETRY, MO is the perpendicular bisector of AB and CO bisects angle ACB. △ AMO = △ BMO (by Case 3 of Similarity), and so ∠ MAO = ∠ MBO.

△ ADO = △ BEO (by the Pythagorean Theorem and Case 3 of Similarity), and so ∠ OAD = ∠ OBE.

Consequently ∠ MAO + ∠ OAD = ∠ MBO + ∠ OBE; ∠ BAC = ∠ ABC; and triangle ABC is isosceles.

15. Starting with triangle ABC in Fig. B in which CB < CA, we wish to expose the fallacy in the foregoing "proof" that purports to show that CB = CA. Since the fault probably lies in the diagram shown in Fig. 9 on page 32 of BASIC GEOMETRY, we had better give careful consideration to the sort of triangle we draw.

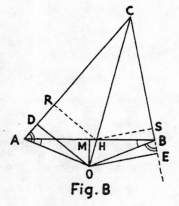

Fig. B

We know from Theorem 28 that ∠CAB must be less than ∠CBA. Consequently ∠CAB must be acute and ∠CBA might conceivably be acute, right, or obtuse. We dismiss the obtuse possibility at once, because if we should succeed in "proving" the theorem under this condition, ∠CAB would have to be obtuse also, which is impossible. For the same reason we dismiss the possibility that ∠CBA is a right angle.

Let us consider next whether the bisector of angle ACB intersects AB to the right or to the left of the mid-point M. If we draw perpendiculars HR and HS from H to CA and CB respectively, then △CHR = △CHS, CR = CS, and AR > BS. Consequently, by the Pythagorean Theorem, AH > HB and H is to the right of M. It follows that the intersection O of MO and CO must be outside the triangle, below AB, and not inside the triangle, as shown in Fig. 9 on page 32. This is the chief error in Fig. 9. If the student sees this, that is all that can fairly be expected of him.

Lastly, we must consider whether the perpendiculars OD and OE meet CA and CB respectively in two points D and E that are both between C and the corresponding vertex of the triangle; or both outside the triangle, on CA and CB extended; or one inside and the other outside. In the first case the purported proof appears still to hold if we subtract the angles instead of adding; namely ∠OAD - ∠MAO = ∠OBE - ∠MBO. In the second case the purported proof appears still to hold, just as given in Ex. 14, by adding the angles. Actually, however, neither of these cases is possible and the apparent proofs have no standing.

We turn now to the third case, shown in Fig. B, in which D lies between C and A and E lies on CB extended. This case is possible. But now we get nothing sensible either by adding or subtracting the angles. If ∠CAB were indeed equal to ∠CBA, then ∠OAD - ∠MAO would equal 180° - (∠OBE + ∠MBO). This would require that ∠OAD should equal 180° - ∠OBE; namely, that the equal angles OAD and OBE should be supplementary, and consequently right angles. This would mean that triangles ADO and BEO would each contain two right angles, which is impossible.

Evidently we cannot prove triangle ABC isosceles so long as we retain the initial condition that CA and CB are unequal.

Page 281: Exercises.

1. (a) Child saw cake.
   (b) Child did not eat cake.
   (c) Children see cakes.
   (d) Children will eat cakes.

2. (a) Man caught boy.
   (b) Man did not spank boy.
   (c) Men catch boys.
   (d) Men will spank boys.

3. (a) Circle was outside of triangle.
   (b) Circle was not inside of triangle.
   (c) Circles are outside of triangles.
   (d) Circles will be inside of triangles.

4. (a) Quotient was greater than divisor.
   (b) Quotient was not less than divisor.
   (c) Quotients are greater than divisors.
   (d) Quotients will be less than divisors.

Pages 282-283: Exercises.

1. Let us assume at the outset that $A < B$. When we shall have completed the proof under this assumption we shall need only to interchange A and B throughout to cover the case $B < A$.

   Given: $A < B$; $K < L$; $A < K < B$; $A < L < B$; and $K < X < L$.

   To prove: $A < X < B$.

   Proof: Since $A < K$ and $K < X$ (both given), we know

   that $A < X$ (Assumption 2).

   Since $X < L$ and $L < B$ (both given), we know

   that $X < B$ (Assumption 2).

   Therefore $A < X < B$ (Assumption 2).

2. **Assumptions:**

(1.) A is older than B, or the same age as B, or younger than B.

(2.) If A is older than B and B is older than C, then A is older than C.

(3.) If A is the same age as B and B is the same age as C, then A is the same age as C.

Theorems:

(1.) If A is older than B and B is older than C and C is older than D, then A is older than D.

(2.) If A is the same age as B and B is older than C, then A is older than C.

3. **Assumptions:**

(1.) A is less than B, or equal to B, or greater than B.

(2.) If A is less than B and B is less than C, then A is less than C.

(3.) If A equals B and B equals C, then A equals C.

Theorems:

(1.) If A is less than B and B is less than C and C is less than D, then A is less than D.

(2.) If A equals B and B is less than C, then A is less than C.

4. **Assumptions:**

(1.) A precedes B, or coincides with B, or follows B.

(2.) If A precedes B and B precedes C, then A precedes C.

(3.) If A coincides with B and B coincides with C, then A coincides with C.

Theorems:

(1.) If A precedes B and B precedes C and C precedes D, then A precedes D.

(2.) If A coincides with B and B precedes C, then A precedes C.

LAWS OF NUMBER

<u>Page 285, line 19</u>: "Real numbers." These are not defined here. The real numbers a, b, c, . . . are strictly merely the undefined elements of this system. Since the system we propose to build is to be concerned with numbers, we think of the elements as numbers and call the system a "number system." The properties these numbers acquire from the system are such that eventually we are moved to call them "real numbers." Thus, although strictly the real numbers remain undefined throughout, in effect the whole system serves, through its postulates and theorems, to characterize them in just the way we want.